D0832973

The Technical Institute

$5.00 Sub. Ser. Co. 6-8-60

# The Technical Institute

LEO F. SMITH
Dean of Instruction,
Rochester Institute
of Technology



LAURENCE LIPSETT
Director, Counseling Center,
Rochester Institute
of Technology

McGRAW-HILL BOOK COMPANY, INC.

1956 NEW YORK TORONTO LONDON

THE TECHNICAL INSTITUTE



*Library of Congress Catalog Card Number:* 55-11571

# Preface

Although technical institutes have existed in the United States for more than one hundred years, most of the information about them has been scattered in a variety of sources, such as institute catalogues, pamphlets, reports of committees, and the memories of technical institute educators. No book of any type has been published concerning the technical institute except for the excellent study made by Wickenden and Spahr in 1931 under the auspices of the Society for the Promotion of Engineering Education (now the American Society for Engineering Education).

A need has often been expressed for a comprehensive book which would bring together the important facts about technical institute education and would outline techniques for planning, initiating, administering, and evaluating technical institute programs.

When the present book was first conceived in 1947, unfamiliarity with the aims and purposes of technical institutes was frequently indicated in comments by members of graduate faculties in education, engineering educators, and the general public. Guidance counselors were at a loss for a source of information about the location and type of technical-terminal programs available. In fact, technical institute educators themselves were uncertain as to how many technical institutes there were and where they were located.

This book has been designed to meet the following objectives: (1) to serve as a definitive work outlining the purposes, present status, and possibilities of technical institute education; (2) to describe techniques which may be utilized to determine the need for this type of education, to organize curriculums, to recruit staff and students, and to administer a technical institute program in all its aspects; and (3) to provide for guidance counselors and prospective students a source of information about the location and nature of the various types of technical institute curriculums.

Many individuals have cooperated wholeheartedly in providing information and material for this book. The authors are indebted to the technical institute administrators who have so faithfully filled out questionnaires for the Annual Survey of Technical Institutes and other purposes. Of the others who have made this book possible we can mention only a few, but our gratitude is sincere and genuine. Among the educators who have made special contributions, we should like to thank Henry P. Adams, H. Russell Beatty, Von Roy Daugherty, Lynn A. Emerson, Kenneth L. Holderman, Lawrence V. Johnson, Harold P. Rodes, Thomas J. Rung, and Karl O. Werwath. Arthur L. Williston has been most helpful in providing perspective and an interpretation of technical institute philosophy. Informal conversations with technical institute educators over a period of years at the annual meetings of the American Society for Engineering Education have provided ideas and inspiration. We should especially like to express our gratitude to L. L. Jarvie, F. E. Almstead, and the directors of the New York State institutes, all of whom over a period of years of friendly association have assisted us in clarifying our concepts of technical institute education.

Close associations and long discussions with department heads and faculty members at the Rochester Institute of Technology have provided an appreciation of the philosophy, objectives, and potentialities of technical institute education. In particular, we should like to thank Mark Ellingson for his inspiring leadership and Ralph W. Tyler for his guidance and criticism.

This book would not have been possible without the patience and care of the several secretaries who typed the manuscript. In closing, we should like to express appreciation of the understanding of our families, who made sacrifices of time, space, and recreation while this book was being completed.

LEO F. SMITH
LAURENCE LIPSETT

# Contents

Preface v

PART ONE The Technical Institute in American Education

1 Introduction 3

What a Technical Institute Is Not. Types of Technical Institutes. What is the Need for Technical Institute Education? Summary.

2 Historical Development 18

Background of the Technical Institute. Early Technical Institutes. Influence of the Engineering College. Role of the Junior College. Significant Developments within the Past Twenty-five Years. The Future of the Technical Institute.

3 Present Status 38

Enrollment Trends since World War II. The Eleventh Annual Survey. Terminal Education in Junior Colleges and Community Colleges. Summary.

4 Curriculums Offered 56

Number and Types of Curriculums Offered. Student Enrollment in Various Curriculums. Technical Institute Graduates. Components of Accredited Curriculums. General Education in the Technical Institute Curriculum. Summary.

5 Careers of Graduates 80

Types of Positions Held. Job Progression. Salary Trends. Transfer Problems. Summary.

PART TWO Organizing and Administering Technical Institute Programs

6 Determining Objectives 103

What Are Objectives? Special Objectives of Technical Institutes. Special Factors Affecting Objectives. Steps in Preparing Objectives. Building a Program.

7 Surveying the Demand 113

The Scope of Technical Occupations. Preliminary Steps in Making a Survey. Survey Methods and Procedures. Determining the Needs for Technical Curriculums. Surveying the Interest of Youth. Summary.

8 Developing Curriculums 129

Approaches to Curriculum Construction. Studying Job Requirements. Activity Analysis and Curriculum Content. Planning Courses of Instruction. The Place of General Education. Planning General Education Content. Typical Technical Institute Curriculums. General Principles.

9 The Instructional Staff 147

Qualifications. Sources of Recruitment. Preparation. In-service Training. Instructional Methods and Materials. Teaching Loads. Summary.

10 Recruiting and Selecting Students 163

How Are Students Recruited? What Recruiting Techniques Are Most Successful? Admissions. Summary.

11 Student Personnel Services 179

Admissions. Orientation. Housing and Food Service. Health Services. Counseling. Remedial Services. Student Activities. Financial Aids and Student Employment. Job-placement Service. Cumulative Student Personnel Records. Summary.

12 Cooperative Education 203

History of Cooperative Education. Cooperative Work Programs. Organizing Cooperative Work Programs. Administering Cooperative Work Programs. Evaluation of Techniques of Administering Cooperative Programs. Coordinating the School and Work Experiences.

13 Administration 222

General Control. Organizational Structure. Finances. Business Administration. Plant. Administering the Instructional Program. Student Personnel Administration. Public Relations. Evaluation. General Principles.

14 The Technical Institute and the Future 244

## APPENDIXES

1 Technical Institute Programs Accredited by the Engineers' Council for Professional Development 249
2 Dates of Founding of Technical Institutes 263
3 Full-time Technical Institute Enrollment by Curriculums 268
4 Check List of Criteria for Identifying Technical Jobs 280
5 Representative Curriculums in Technical Institutes 282
6 In-service Course 291
7 Freshman Questionnaire 293
8 Questionnaire on Teaching Effectiveness 297
9 Representative Organizational Charts of Technical Institutes 299

Index 309

# PART ONE

## The Technical Institute in American Education

CHAPTER 1

# Introduction

There has been a tendency to conceive of the American educational system as a single ladder leading from elementary school through the university. In this conception the positions of the elementary school, secondary school, college, and university have become quite clearly crystallized.

The technical institute, however, is one type of institution which does not fit clearly into the single-ladder scheme. It is the purpose of this book to define the technical institute, to explain its functions, to outline its present place in American education, and to survey the principles and techniques of establishing technical institute curriculums.

A technical institute is a postsecondary institution whose curriculums (1) are of one to three years' duration, (2) are technological in character, and (3) emphasize understanding and application of scientific principles more than manual skills.

Technical institutes first developed in the United States under private auspices in response to local educational needs. Naturally there was wide diversity in their characteristics and programs.

The first definitive study of technical institute education in the United States was published in 1931. This study was authorized by the Board of Investigation and Coordination of the Society for the Promotion of Engineering Education (SPEE). William E. Wickenden was Director of Investigations and was assisted by Robert H. Spahr. This study is commonly referred to as the Wickenden-Spahr Report.[1] This committee found that the characteristics of a technical institute may be summarized as follows:[2]

1. It is a school of postsecondary character, but distinct in character from a college or university.

2. Its purpose is to train men and women for callings and functions which occupy an area between the skilled crafts and the highly scientific professions. A fair proportion of those trained advance in time to professional status.

3. It caters principally to persons who through either previous or collateral experience in industry have found their bearings and desire intensive preparation for chosen lines of progress.

4. It offers training both for technical pursuits, concerned with planning and control, and for supervisory pursuits, concerned with operation and maintenance. The engineering college more largely emphasizes the former

[1] William E. Wickenden and Robert H. Spahr, *A Study of Technical Institutes,* Society for the Promotion of Engineering Education, Lancaster, Pa., 1931.

[2] *Ibid.,* pp. 17–18.

group; the technical institute, on the other hand, emphasizes the latter.

5. Being intensive in purpose, its courses are shorter in duration than those of the professional colleges. They are essentially terminal rather than preparatory courses.

6. Being a school without academic standardization, its admission and graduation requirements are less formal than those of the colleges and stress capacity and experience more than credit units.

7. Its methods of teaching are relatively direct, with a strong emphasis on doing as distinct from book study.

8. Its teachers, while possessing adequate scholarly preparation, are chosen primarily on the basis of practical experience, personal sagacity, and ability to teach through programs of orderly experience.

9. Its entire scheme of instruction follows much more closely the actual usage of industry than that of professional engineering schools.

The characteristics listed above are still applicable twenty years later in outlining the essential nature of the technical institute. Over the years, however, there has been some shift of emphasis. As the field of technical institute education has gradually crystallized, there has been increasing standardization of admission and graduation requirements. The curriculums are designed to be terminal, and the graduate is prepared for "immediate employment in a relatively restricted activity."[3] Student person-

[3] C. W. Beese, "The Technical Institute: Its Relation to Engineering Education and Trade Training," *J. Engng. Educ.*, vol. 8, p. 237, December, 1952.

nel services have broadened, and the amount of general education has increased.

The Wickenden-Spahr study[4] found need for further development of education of the technical institute type for two main reasons:

1. Other institutions, such as engineering colleges, are inadequate for meeting the personnel needs of industry, particularly with respect to "line" supervision.

2. The aims of engineering colleges are confused when they attempt to meet needs of this type. One of this study's findings was that "in the light of experience, both in America and Europe, these schools should have their own distinctive character and direction in order to achieve a permanent success."[5] This need was also felt by most technical institute personnel.

As an outgrowth of long interest in technical institute curriculums on the part of the Engineers' Council for Professional Development (EPCD), a meeting of technical institute representatives was finally held in 1940 to discuss accreditation. This meeting voted to request ECPD to set up procedures and criteria for accrediting technical institutes, but four years of war intervened before final action was completed. Meanwhile the National Council of Technical Schools, comprised mainly of proprietary institutions, set up its own accrediting procedure.

In 1945, its first year of technical institute accreditation activity, the ECPD accredited curriculums in seven institutions. Curriculums are now accredited in a total of

[4] Wickenden and Spahr, *op. cit.*, pp. 2, 3.
[5] *Ibid.*, p. 1.

twenty-seven institutions.[6] The ECPD requirements for accredited curriculums are:[7]

1. *Duration.* Not less than one academic year of full-time work or the equivalent in part-time work.

2. *Requirements for admission.* High school graduation or the equivalent.

3. *Curriculums.* Technological in nature, employing the application of physical science and the techniques of mathematics to the solution of practical problems, and comprising a prescribed sequence of related courses in a specific field, though not excluding a reasonable amount of elective subject matter.

4. *Instruction.* By accepted class and laboratory or correspondence methods. Except in programs which may be properly offered by correspondence, laboratory work shall comprise an important part of each curriculum.

5. *Teaching staff.* Qualified as to educational training and experience and sufficient in numbers to provide adequate attention to each student.

6. *Educational institution.* An organized school or a division of an institution or industry devoted to the specific aim of providing technical institute programs; a stable organization having adequate financial support and demonstrated capacity and achievement in the technical institute field.

7. *Physical facilities.* Adequate for the purposes of the curriculums offered.

[6] *Technical Institute Programs in the United States, 1954,* Engineers' Council for Professional Development, New York, 1954.

[7] *Ibid.*, pp. 46–47.

## What a technical institute is not

It will be seen in the foregoing that the technical institute in a sense occupies a position between the vocational and technical high school on the one hand and the engineering college on the other hand. This intermediate position and the diversity of technical institute programs have led to considerable confusion and misunderstanding regarding the purposes and characteristics of technical institutes. In this connection it is important to clarify what the technical institute is *not*.

Confusion of technical institutes with vocational and technical high schools stems from the period when the early technical institutes to some extent filled the role that is now filled by high schools. In the days when the public high schools offered nothing but a college preparatory curriculum, some of the technical institutes had curriculums in woodworking, machine shop, and other branches of the skilled trades. For such curriculums the institutes accepted students who were not high school graduates. The general education component was either absent or minimal. In short, the technical institutes which followed this pattern were performing functions that are now considered the proper province of the secondary school.

As the technical institutes have developed a more clear-cut pattern and found a more stable position in the educational structure, it is possible to distinguish them from secondary schools in several important ways. The technical institute admission requirement of high school graduation assures a more mature student. The technical institute pays less attention to training in skills and emphasizes the "why" as well as the "how" of an occupation through adequate study of college level mathematics, chemistry, and physics.[8] Such high school subjects as algebra and geometry are now typical prerequisites for technological courses in technical institutes. The more advanced technical institutes often begin their work in mathematics with college algebra and proceed through integral calculus. Some of the technical institutes still offer preparation for the skilled trades, but these curriculums are not now considered true technical institute programs and would not qualify for accreditation. In many technical institute curriculums a certain amount of trade training is included, but this is mainly as a supplement to the technical courses.

Some of the courses taught in technical institutes are comparable to those taught in engineering colleges, but there are important differences between the two kinds of institutions. As the ECPD Subcommittee on Technical Institutes states of institutes:[9]

> . . . the scope of the programs is more limited than that required to prepare for a career as a professional engineer . . . programs of instruction are briefer, and usually more completely technical in content than professional curricula, though they are concerned with the same general fields of industry and engineering. They do not lead to the baccalaureate degree in engineering. Such designations as En-

[8] Cf. Beese, *op. cit.,* p. 237.
[9] ECPD, *op. cit.,* p. 46.

gineering Aide, Technical Aide, Associate in Engineering, and Engineering Associate are appropriate designations to be conferred upon graduates of programs of technical institute type.

There is another group of specialized trade schools which may be distinguished clearly from technical institutes as the latter are defined in this chapter. These schools, most of which are operated for profit, have curriculums in skilled trades such as radio and television repair, diesel repair (as distinguished from diesel technology), piano tuning, and watch repair (as distinguished from horology). These specialized schools ordinarily teach only the minimum essentials necessary to perform the occupation at the journeyman level. They do not usually broaden their courses with general education subjects or with mathematics and science apart from the trade or craft itself. Many of these specialized courses are less than one year in length. High school graduation is much less likely to be a prerequisite. For the most part, the specialized schools prepare graduates for only one job, while technical institutes prepare graduates for a cluster of jobs.

## Types of technical institutes

In the foregoing, the technical institute has been defined as a type of institution. The first institution of this nature was Ohio Mechanics Institute, founded in 1828, with private endowment and support. In more recent years technical institutes have found other means of support, and curriculums of a technical institute type have also developed in a number of other types of institutions.

Curriculums within the scope of the technical institute definition are now found in the following types of institutions:

1. Technical institutes primarily offering curriculums of the technical institute type. These institutes have three principal means of support:
   *a.* Public support, by states or municipalities, as exemplified by the institutes operated by the states of New York and New Hampshire.
   *b.* Private endowment and support, with nonprofit operation, such as Franklin Technical Institute and Wentworth Institute in Boston, Rochester Institute of Technology, and Ohio Mechanics Institute.
   *c.* Proprietary institutions, operated for profit, like Capitol Radio Engineering Institute, the Academy of Aeronautics, and Central Technical Institute.
2. Separate on-campus divisions of institutions which also offer professional engineering programs. The University of Houston and Oklahoma Agricultural and Mechanical College have divisions of this type.
3. Off-campus centers operated under the auspices of colleges and universities. Georgia Institute of Technology, Purdue University, and the Pennsylvania State University operate such centers.
4. Schools or training divisions operated by or in close affiliation with industries, such as Northrop Aeronautical Institute and RCA Institutes.
5. Evening sessions of colleges and universities, as exemplified by Fenn College.

6. Junior colleges offering terminal programs, such as Pasadena Junior College, Los Angeles City College, and New Haven YMCA Junior College.
7. Correspondence schools, either proprietary or extension divisions of colleges and universities.

Many institutions offering curriculums of the technical institute type also have a wide variety of other terminal curriculums which are not technological in the usual sense of the term. Examples of such curriculums are retailing, art, home economics, agriculture, dental hygiene, and business administration. To keep the scope of this book within reasonable bounds, attention will be given primarily to curriculums of a definitely technological nature, following the criteria of ECPD. In its 1952–1953 report ECPD listed accredited technical institute curriculums under a variety of titles in the following general fields:[10]

Air Conditioning, Heating, and Refrigeration
Aircraft Technology (including design, construction, drafting)
Automobile Repair and Service Management
Civil Technology
Diesel Technology
Electrical Technology
Fire Protection
Industrial Chemistry
Mechanical Technology (including machine and tool design and drafting)
Photographic Technology

[10] ECPD, *op. cit.,* pp. 48–51.

Radio and Television Technology
Stationary Engineering (including steam and diesel)
Structural Technology
Welding Technology

Appendix 1 lists the technical institute programs accredited by ECPD.

The responses to the tenth annual survey of technical institutes revealed a total of 213 curriculums which could be classified in twenty-two major areas.[11] These included both accredited and unaccredited curriculums, and further information will be presented about these in Chapter 4.

**What is the need for technical institute education?**

The primary purpose of the technical institute is to prepare graduates for employment in certain technical and supervisory occupations. The need for this type of education depends upon (1) the numbers of people in these occupations, (2) the annual need for new workers for replacement or expansion, and (3) other sources of trained personnel.

As long ago as 1926 four separate surveys of industrial plants in New Jersey and California revealed that more technical institute graduates are needed than four-year engineering college graduates in ratios ranging from 2.6 to 1 to 2.8 to 1.[12] At that time the actual ratio of technicians to engineers was 1 to 5.

[11] Leo F. Smith, "Annual Survey of Technical Institutes 1953–54," *Tech. Educ. News,* August, 1954, p. 1.
[12] Wickenden and Spahr, *op. cit.,* pp. 53–59.

The increasing need for the technical institute types of education is indicated by a comparison of the 1926 figures with data gathered from 16 states in 1944. Emerson reports that the numbers of technicians required per college-trained engineer ranged from 2.2 to 1 in industrial chemistry to 20.0 to 1 in wood processing. The average for all industries surveyed was 5.2 to 1.[13] The present ratio is one technician to three engineering graduates, which is still in inverse relationship to the need.[14] In the manufacturing field, the present status of sources of personnel and the desired status are shown in Table 1.

In 1945 a survey was made to determine the need for technical institute education in New York State. It was found that manufacturing industries employed approximately 1,000,000 persons, of whom 9 per cent were engaged in technical occupations.[15] Nonmanufacturing industries employed about 2,500,000 persons, of whom nearly 11 per cent were engaged in technical occupations. On the basis of a 5 per cent annual replacement, it was estimated that New York State would need 17,600 additional technicians each year.[16]

At the present time most technicians are recruited from employees experienced on the job or from the ranks

[13] *Vocational-Technical Training for Industrial Occupations,* U.S. Office of Education Bulletin 228, Washington, 1944, p. x.

[14] Edward E. Booher, "Technical Institute Comes of Age," *J. Engng. Educ.,* vol. 42, p. 338, March, 1952.

[15] J. Cayce Morrison, *A Guide to the Development of Programs for the Institutes of Applied Arts and Sciences,* University of the State of New York, Albany, 1946, p. 31.

[16] *Ibid.*

TABLE 1

PRESENT AND DESIRED STATUS OF TECHNICAL INSTITUTE PERSONNEL

| Source of Personnel | Supervisory and Technical Forces | | Total Forces in Manufacture | |
|---|---|---|---|---|
| | Present Status (Per cent) | Desired Status (Per cent) | Present Status (Per cent) | Desired Status (Per cent) |
| Technical institute graduates | 0.8 | 46.0 | 0.1 | 6.0 |
| College graduates | 13.0 | 17.0 | 1.7 | 2.2 |
| From ranks and other training | 86.2 | 37.0 | 98.2 | 91.8 |
| | 100.0 | 100.0 | 100.0 | 100.0 |

SOURCE: *Vocational-Technical Training for Industrial Occupations*, U.S. Office of Education Bulletin 228, Washington, 1944, p. x.

of recent college graduates seeking initial employment. The New York State survey committee, however, estimated that 75 per cent of the annual replacements in technician jobs would be filled by technical institute graduates if there were an adequate system of institutions.

Study after study has shown a need for technical institute education which greatly exceeded the offerings available. The more recent surveys particularly suggest that the pattern of industrial development is bringing about an increasing demand for this type of education. In response to this demand, eleven new technical institutes have been established in the past six years.[17]

[17] Booher, *op. cit.*, p. 342.

## Summary

After more than a century of development, the technical institute is finally establishing an increasingly important, clear-cut place for itself in American education. Although it has been a type of institution which does not fit clearly into the single-ladder scheme of American education, there are several distinctive characteristics which have been pointed out in this chapter:

1. It is a postsecondary institution whose curriculums
   *a.* Are one to three years in length
   *b.* Are technological in character
   *c.* Emphasize understanding and application of scientific principles more than manual skills
2. It is not a technical high school; neither is it an engineering college. High school graduation is required for entrance, and mathematics through geometry and algebra are typical prerequisites for technological courses. On the other hand, the programs of instruction are briefer and usually more completely technical in content than the professional engineering curriculums.
3. Technical institute curriculums are offered in a variety of institutions as follows:
   *a.* Institutions which call themselves technical institutes and which may have public support, be privately endowed, or be operated as proprietary institutions
   *b.* Separate on-campus or off-campus divisions of colleges and universities also offering professional engineering programs

   *c.* Schools or training divisions operating in close affiliation with industries
   *d.* Evening sessions of colleges and universities
   *e.* Junior colleges offering terminal programs
   *f.* Correspondence schools—either proprietary or extension divisions of colleges and universities
4. There is a real and increasing need for the technical institute type of education. Studies in 1926 indicated that the number of technical institute graduates required was 2.6 to 2.8 for each college-trained engineer. In 1944 Emerson found that this ratio ranged from 2.2 to 1 in industrial chemistry to 20.0 to 1 in wood-processing, with an average for all industries surveyed of 5.2 to 1.

CHAPTER 2

# Historical Development

In colonial America mass production as it is known today did not exist. More than 95 per cent of the population was agricultural and for the most part, the skills and knowledge required in farming were passed on from father to son without formal training. The few skilled craftsmen of this period received their training as apprentices.

The social and economic forces which gave rise to the technical institute began to find expression in the academy founded in 1751 by Franklin, who sought the improvement of agriculture, industry, and commerce through the application of science and reason. Alongside the Latin grammar schools of English heritage there began to develop a number of secondary schools offering courses in practical aspects of mathematics, bookkeeping, surveying, navigation, and other vocational subjects.

With the growth of the urban population which came as a result of the industrial revolution, there arose in both Britain and America a movement for the welfare and education of the workingman. One aspect of this movement was represented by the mechanics' institutes which

vere founded in the 1820s in New York, Boston, Balti-
nore, Cincinnati, and Philadelphia. They sought the
'promotion of the useful arts" and the cultural and voca-
ional development of their members through lectures,
ibraries, and classes. Eventually, however, the spread of
ree public education and changing culture patterns
ended to eliminate the need for this type of education.

The only one of these early mechanics' institutes which
volved into the type of technical institute with which this
ook deals was the Ohio Mechanics Institute, founded
n 1828.[1]

## Background of the technical institute

In the early American economy, dominated by farmers
nd artisans, there was no real need for education of the
echnical institute type. Apprenticeship was both appro-
riate and adequate for meeting the needs of the society in
espect to vocational skills. As industrialization spread, the
eeds for skilled workers were filled to a considerable
xtent by journeymen trained in Europe, where appren-
iceship had greater scope and prestige.

The changing patterns of industry after the Civil War
rovided a direct impetus toward education of the tech-
ical institute type. Free lands and a variety of employ-
nent opportunities tended to make young men unwilling
) enter into apprenticeship arrangements which would
ind them for several years. Mass production tended to

[1] The Mechanics Institute in New York City, founded in 1820,
an almost qualify as a modern technical institute. Its evening pro-
rams are technical institute in character, if not in duration.

increase the percentage of unskilled and semiskilled labor.

However, the more industrialized economy began to need more draftsmen, supervisors, designers, production planners, and other technical personnel. Advancement on the job was unsatisfactory as a means of filling manpower needs of this type. Neither the secondary schools of the period nor the engineering colleges were attempting to meet these needs directly. As a result, groups of manufacturers in a number of industrial cities began to establish technical institutes to provide a supply of supervisory and technical personnel and to broaden the opportunities of local young men.

## Early technical institutes

The pioneer American institution of a definite technical institute type was the Gardiner (Maine) Lyceum, established in 1822.[2] The original two-year course of study was extended to three years. It included bookkeeping, algebra, geometry, trigonometry, surveying, navigation, calculus, chemistry, linear drawing, political economy, and natural philosophy. Part of the support of this institution came from the state legislature, which ceased its appropriations after ten years, perhaps because the institution may have been ahead of its time.

As mentioned previously, Ohio Mechanics Institute is the oldest of the present-day technical institutes. A booklet published in recognition of the 125th anniversary describes

[2] William E. Wickenden and Robert H. Spahr, *A Study of Technical Institutes,* Society for the Promotion of Engineering Education, Lancaster, Pa., 1931.

some of the significant factors in the early history of this institution:[3]

> The need for such training in Cincinnati was recognized early in the nineteenth century. Before the Institute came into being, libraries had been formed for the education of its residents, the Circulating Library Society having been incorporated in 1812 for general use and the Apprentices Library founded in 1821 for the benefit of "young persons engaged in mechanical or other laborious employments." In the Autumn of 1828 John D. Craig delivered a course of lectures on natural philosophy and suggested the establishment here of a Mechanics Institute. In furtherance of this plan four men called a public meeting to consider the matter. . . . At the meeting it was decided that such an Institute should be founded and a committee was appointed.
>
> The second meeting, held on 20th November 1828, was significant . . . because of . . . the approval of the committee's report and the adoption of the constitution.

Evidently the members of this committee were men of action, for[4]

> . . . within three months the Ohio Mechanics Institute was granted a charter and incorporated by the state's General Assembly "for advancing the best interests of the mechanics, manufacturers, and artisans by the more general

[3] *A History of the Ohio Mechanics Institute: Cincinnati 1828–1953,* Bulletin of the Historical and Philosophical Society of Ohio, vol. 2, no. 3, p. 4, July, 1953.

[4] *Ibid.,* p. 5.

diffusion of useful knowledge in those important classes of the community." . . . Courses in arithmetic, geometry and chemistry were offered in that first winter and were well attended, the courses meeting in rooms of other schools and in the City Council Chamber on Fourth Street.

The sailing was not entirely smooth for this new institution; it was forced to move from place to place and had many financial problems down through the years. Despite these vicissitudes, the present Ohio Mechanics Institute traces its history back to 1828, thus making it the oldest of the present-day technical institutes.

Pratt Institute, one of the best known of the early institutes, was opened in October, 1877, to a group of only twelve students. Under the wise leadership of Charles Pratt, the founder, the institution prospered, beginning with the School of Science and Technology. Schools of Fine and Applied Arts, Library Science, Kindergarten Training, and Household Science were later added. Pratt Institute was[5]

> . . . unique among educational institutions in having a Board of Trustees consisting at the present time of five sons, and seven grandsons of the Founder, who have interested themselves to an extraordinary degree in promoting all that Pratt Institute stands for . . . in erecting additional buildings and adding to the endowment as occasion has required.

Gradually Pratt Institute changed from technical institute programs to traditional baccalaureate degree courses.

The Rochester Institute of Technology, formerly the

[5] Walter S. Perry, *Pratt Institute: Its Beginning and Development,* Pratt Institute, Brooklyn, 1953, p. 23.

Rochester Athenaeum and Mechanics Institute, traces its history back to 1829, when the Rochester Athenaeum was founded "to enrich the cultural life of the community." In 1885, Mechanics Institute was founded to provide training for the young men and women of the community in the industrial arts and in homemaking. Six years later, in 1891, the Athenaeum and the Mechanics Institute merged, and this institution has been a dynamic force in the Rochester community since that time.[6] In 1944 the name was changed to the Rochester Institute of Technology.

Wentworth Institute in Boston was founded through the gift of Arioch Wentworth "for the purpose of furnishing education in the Mechanical Arts." The Institute opened for instruction in September, 1911, and through the years has adhered to the original concepts of the founder. This institution has been one of the leaders in the technical institute field, first under the leadership of Arthur L. Williston, who served as principal from 1911 to 1924, and later under Frederick E. Dobbs, who served in the same capacity from 1924 to 1952.[7]

Spring Garden Institute, founded in 1851, and Franklin Technical Institute, founded in 1908, are two of the older more substantial privately endowed institutes that are still active today.

[6] George W. Hoke, *Blazing New Trails,* Rochester Athenaeum and Mechanics Institute, Rochester, N.Y., 1937.

[7] Orvis H. Saxby, *Wentworth Institute, 1904–1954: A Review of its Founding and Fifty Years of Progress,* Wentworth Alumni Association, Boston, 1954, pp. 7–8.

During the same period that gave rise to the privately endowed institutes, proprietary schools were founded to meet similar needs. Among the more substantial of these early proprietary institutes were those which will be described briefly below.

Bliss Electrical School was founded in 1893 by Louis D. Bliss, who remained as active president for more than fifty-five years.[8] This institute offered work primarily in the electrical field, and by 1948 had trained more than 10,000 men for technical work in the electrical field. The school closed its doors in 1950, and the buildings and grounds have now been taken over by the Montgomery Junior College, a publicly supported community college.

The Milwaukee School of Engineering is another example of an institution founded by a dynamic individual, Oscar Werwath. This institute first opened its doors in 1903 to provide technical training in the electrical field. One of the significant contributions which this school has made has been the concept of the concentric curriculum. Karl Werwath, president of the school since his father's death in 1948, has described this curriculum as follows:[9]

> Contrary to usual procedure, the concentric curriculum works from practice to theory, rather than from theory to practice. It encompasses training on three levels: service-vocational; technician-semiprofessional; and engineering-professional. The program is geared to the college level, but be-

[8] "Technical Institute Profiles: Bliss Electrical School," *Tech. Educ. News,* October, 1948, pp. 5–8.

[9] "Technical Institute Profiles: Milwaukee School of Engineering," *Tech. Educ. News,* October, 1950, p. 5.

cause it provides successive terminal points, every student has an opportunity to reach his ultimate potential.

In later years the Milwaukee School of Engineering has changed from a proprietary to a privately endowed institution.

At a fairly early date certain states also began to take an interest in this type of education. This led to the establishment of technical institute courses in Massachusetts, California, Iowa, Idaho, and Wisconsin. A number of institutions of various types also developed evening courses of the technical institute type.

The exhaustive study published by the SPEE in 1931, although it did not claim to be complete, listed thirty-four institutions, of which only nine were "predominantly technical institutes." Fifteen were predominantly degree-granting colleges or universities, and ten were "industrial schools of mixed character." Full-time day courses were offered by nineteen of the thirty-four institutions, and evening courses were offered by fourteen.[10]

Appendix 2 lists the most accurate data which the authors have been able to obtain on the dates of founding of the present-day technical institutes.

### Influence of the engineering college

The same social and economic forces that led to the development of technical institutes brought about the establishment of a school at Troy, New York, which had for its primary objective the training of teachers of tech-

[10] Wickenden and Spahr, *op. cit.*, pp. 40–45.

nical subjects. Established in 1823, this institution came along just in time for the first tremendous spurt of railroad building. By 1835 the school, which was to become Rensselaer Polytechnic Institute, had evolved an engineering curriculum patterned on contemporary French models and had granted its first degree in civil engineering. By 1840, Union College, Dartmouth, Yale, Harvard, and the University of Michigan had established four-year curriculums in engineering or applied science.[11]

In some respects the early engineering curriculums did not enjoy the social prestige of liberal arts education at the college level. But almost from the outset, the engineering courses conformed to traditional patterns in the sense that a secondary school graduate could obtain a bachelor's degree in four years of higher education.

The Morrill Act of 1862, which assigned certain federal lands to the states for the establishment of land-grant colleges, was another important factor in developing American technical education along the lines of the conventional engineering college. To a considerable extent graduates of the land-grant institutions inherited the social prestige and economic advantages which had come to be associated with college degrees.

A number of states which had established technical institute curriculums abandoned them to concentrate upon four-year engineering courses. Some of the private technical institutes followed suit. As shown in an unpublished paper by Arthur L. Williston, formerly Director of the School of Science and Technology of Pratt Institute,

[11] Wickenden and Spahr, *op. cit.*, p. 34.

conspicuous among institutions which, in whole or in part, changed from technical institute programs to traditional engineering curriculums leading to the bachelor's degree are Illinois Institute of Technology, Drexel Institute, Brooklyn Polytechnic Institute, Cooper Union, Pratt Institute, Carnegie Institute of Technology, Bradley Polytechnic Institute, Rose Polytechnic Institute, and Clarkson College of Technology. In September, 1954, the Rochester Institute of Technology, while retaining its terminal three-year cooperative technical institute curriculums, added a "topping program," in which a technical institute graduate may continue for a fourth and fifth year to earn a B.S. degree.

Several colleges and universities have established technical institute programs as separate schools or divisions; sometimes these have been on campus, in other cases off campus. Among the better known which are offering full-time day programs are those operated by Pennsylvania State University, Purdue University, Oklahoma A. and M., the University of Houston, and Southern Technical Institute of the Georgia Institute of Technology. H. P. Adams, Director of the School of Technical Training at Oklahoma A. and M. has thoughtfully outlined the principles at issue when technical institute courses are offered at degree-granting institutions, and the most important recommendation he has to make is as follows:[12]

> Although the program may be under the supervision of engineering administrators, it is extremely important that a

[12] H. P. Adams, "Technical-Institute Programs at Degree-granting Institutions," *Tech. Educ. News,* June, 1951, p. 2.

technical-institute program offered at a four-year institution be set up and operated as a separate organization having its own distinctive character and purpose. The usual charge that these terminal programs will become dumping grounds for failures from the four-year courses, and that they will not attract persons of genuine promise, depends entirely upon the organization and policies adopted.

## Role of the junior college

Junior colleges developed mainly in the West, in response to needs that were more educational than economic, and these institutions were often considered extensions of secondary education. Technical institutes, on the other hand, had originated in the East, deriving impetus from forces that were primarily economic.

When President William Rainey Harper, of the University of Chicago, first coined the term "junior college" in 1896, he conceived that this type of institution would be terminal in the education of a large percentage of students.[13] Nevertheless, junior college courses at first tended to bear close resemblance to those offered in the first two years of four-year liberal arts institutions.

As the American population moved westward, the economic needs which fostered technical institute growth in the East began to be felt west of the Mississippi. With junior colleges already on the educational scene, it was natural that these institutions should attempt to develop

[13] Walter Crosby Eells, *Present Status of Junior College Terminal Education,* American Association of Junior Colleges, Washington, 1941, p. 15.

curriculums of the technical institute type, but at first the purely liberal arts influences prevailed. Viewing junior college efforts up to 1931, the SPEE study concluded, "There is no basis in experience for expecting the junior college of mixed character to do the work of a technical institute successfully."[14]

Within the past two decades, however, the junior colleges have developed an increasing awareness of the need for preparing youth for occupational and civic competence. In 1939 the American Association of Junior Colleges (AAJC) obtained financial support from the General Education Board for a study on terminal education. This was inaugurated in 1940 and was carried on for five years. Several publications emerged from this study, all of which are evidence that the junior college educators are more and more accepting the preparation for occupational competence as one of their most important objectives.[15,16] Some of the most vigorous work in the development of technical-terminal curriculums is currently being carried on by junior colleges.

There appears to be a trend toward decreasing the sharpness of difference between the technical institute and the junior college. Although there are still many differences between a pure junior or community college and a pure technical institute, there are present numerous simi-

[14] Wickenden and Spahr, *op. cit.*, p. 9.

[15] Eells, *op. cit.*, also, *The Literature of Junior College Terminal Education* and *Why Junior College Terminal Education,* American Association of Junior Colleges, Washington, 1941.

[16] Phebe Ward, *Terminal Education in the Junior College,* Harper & Brothers, New York, 1947.

larities. Both Bogue and Booher have expressed the belief that the two types of institutions will move more closely together in their purposes and outlook. Bogue, who is Executive Secretary of the American Association of Junior Colleges, has stated it this way:[17]

> It may be concluded that there is insistent demand and need for ever-increasing numbers of men and women in semiprofessional occupations; that their programs of education must provide for unified and integrated curricula of general and vocational-technical instruction and training; that the flow of students into more advanced fields of study can be effected by better understanding and cooperation between junior colleges and technical institutes on the one hand and the colleges of engineering and other types of higher professional schools on the other . . . that the junior-college program and the technical institute program are aimed at essentially the same goals, each having a great deal to offer the other, and that a closer cooperation and rapprochement between the two should be created.

Booher has made his prediction in the following words:[18]

> The community college is a potent, dynamic force in American education. Its strong aggressive leadership is casting covetous eyes on the field of technical-terminal education, so much so, I feel, that this type of institution may in

[17] Jesse P. Bogue, *The Community College,* McGraw-Hill Book Company, Inc., New York, 1950, p. 205.

[18] Edward E. Booher, "Technical Institute Comes of Age," *J. Engng. Educ.,* vol. 8, p. 338, March, 1952.

the future assume the function of the technical institute as we have known it.

It is clear that the traditional technical institute function is currently being performed very adequately by junior colleges in some communities, particularly in the West. On the other hand there are indications not only that the well-established technical institutes will continue to be indispensable in meeting important educational and industrial needs, but also that institutions of this type will continue to increase in numbers and enrollment.

## Significant developments within the past twenty-five years

Although the present-day technical institutes can trace their history back to the founding of Ohio Mechanics Institute in 1828, the past twenty-five years has undoubtedly seen a more rapid development of the technical institute movement than any other quarter century. At the present time the following are some of the most significant developments which have accelerated the growth of interest in this type of education:

1. The SPEE Study of Technical Institutes.
2. The accreditation of technical institute curriculums by ECPD.
3. The establishment of the Technical Institute Division of the American Society for Engineering Education (ASEE).
4. The organization of the National Council of Technical Schools.

5. The growth of a body of literature on the technical institute movement.

6. The granting of the Associate degree for the completion of technical institute programs.

7. The McGraw-Hill award to outstanding technical institute educators.

Booher has outlined most of these in his excellent article and the authors are indebted to him for many of the ideas which follow.[19]

*The SPEE study of technical institutes*

As this study has already been quoted at some length in Chapter 1, it does not seem appropriate to describe it at length here. It appears, however, that this study, which was carried on as a collateral project to the investigation of engineering education conducted from 1923 to 1929, served as a spark that ignited the present-day interest in technical institutes.

*The accreditation of technical institute curriculums by ECPD*

Certainly one of the most important single factors contributing to the increasing status of technical institute education has been the accreditation of curriculums in these institutions by ECPD. A group of institutes petitioned this engineering body for assistance in 1940. In 1944 a subcommittee on technical institutes of ECPD was appointed and in 1945, Dean H. P. Hammond, the first chairman of this committee, announced that applications

[19] Booher, *loc. cit.*

for accreditation of technical institute curriculums would be received. Under his wise and sympathetic leadership the movement prospered and in the 1954 Annual Report of ECPD, a total of eighty-four curriculums in twenty-seven institutes were listed as approved.

### *The Technical Institute Division of the ASEE*

Occurring as a collateral movement with ECPD accreditation was the establishment of a Division in the ASEE devoted solely to the technical institutes. The first meeting of this Division was held in 1941 at the ASEE meetings in Ann Arbor and attended by a handful of individuals. The passing years, however, have seen an increasing interest, and at the 1953 meetings at the University of Florida and the 1954 meetings at the University of Illinois, approximately 150 individuals attended one or more meetings. Each year this Division has a well-planned program with papers and discussions of interest to educators in this field. Another step forward was taken at the conclusion of the 1953 meetings, when *Technical Education News* undertook the responsibility of publishing all the papers which had been presented.

### *The National Council of Technical Schools*

This organization was formed in 1943 with the objective of the improvement of educational and business standards. It is composed primarily of proprietary institutes although two or three privately endowed schools hold associate memberships. This Council has had an extremely salutary effect on raising the ethical standards in the private school field. Most of the officers of the National Council have also been very active in the Technical Institute Division of the ASEE.

### *The growth of a body of literature on the technical institute movement*

Another evidence of the maturation of the technical institute movement is the body of literature in this field. The committee on Technical Institute Studies of the Technical Institute Division of the ASEE has recently compiled a bibliography[20] listing 267 articles, 39 books, and 64 graduate studies which had appeared through August, 1953. Thus for the first time the most important literature in the field has been indexed.

The regular publication of *Technical Education News* with its wide distribution has stimulated interest in the entire field of technical education and has made possible the publication of many articles on technical institutes.

### *The granting of the Associate degree*

The American public is degree-conscious and has come to expect that the completion of a post–high school program would lead to a degree. The 1931 SPEE Study pointed out the lack of recognized credentials as a distinct handicap to graduates. A Committee on Completion Credentials of the Technical Institute Division, ASEE, has

[20] *Literature Significant to Education of the Technical Institute Type: An Annotated Bibliography,* Committee on Technical Institute Studies, Technical Institute Division, American Society for Engineering Education, New York, 1953.

given long and careful thought to this problem and at the 1952 meeting at Dartmouth passed a resolution urging that the parent body recognize the Associate degree as the appropriate title of accomplishment. The ASEE did appoint a Committee on Designation of Degrees in Colleges of Engineering and Technical Institutes. At the 1955 meetings of the ASEE this Committee recommended to the General Council that the Associate degree be recognized, but no final action was taken by the Council. Regardless of what the decision of the Council may be, it is already an accomplished fact that at least forty-four of the forty-eight states now permit the granting of the Associate degree for two years of post–high school study.

*The McGraw-Hill Award*

The last significant development to be included in this list is the establishment of the James H. McGraw Award, which is made annually in recognition of outstanding contributions in the field of technical institute education. Established in 1950, it has resulted in considerable publicity. It has been awarded as follows:

1950 H. P. Hammond, late Dean of Engineering, Penn State University.
1951 Robert H. Spahr, formerly of General Motors Institute
1952 Arthur Williston, former Principal, Wentworth Institute
1953 Charles W. Beese, Dean, Technical Extension Division, Purdue University

1954 Arthur Harper, former President, Wyomissing Polytechnic Institute

1955 Frederick E. Dobbs, former Principal, Wentworth Institute

## The future of the technical institute

In light of the significant developments which have been outlined above, certain trends with respect to the future of the technical institute appear discernible:

1. There is a trend toward the broadening of objectives and offering of more work in general education. This contrasts with the original technical institute objective of providing technical education leading solely toward occupational competence without too much concern for general education.

2. Another trend, as revealed by the annual surveys of technical institutes, is that more attention is being devoted to adult education. A wider range of courses is being offered and more adults are being enrolled.

3. It is also apparent that there is increasing public support for the technical institute type of education. Within the past decade public-supported institutes have been founded in Connecticut, Georgia, Indiana, New Hampshire, New York, Oklahoma, Oregon, and Pennsylvania.

4. The evidence of the past twenty-five years strongly suggests that technical institutes will increase in size and number in the years which lie ahead. This trend is further indicated by the tremendous increase in the number of youth who will reach college age by 1960, 1965, and 1970.

A recent national study[21] revealed that for the United States there would be an increase over 1953 of 16 per cent by 1960, 46 per cent by 1965, and 70 per cent by 1970. With the increasing recognition being given to this type of education by industrialists and educators, it appears certain that larger numbers will enroll in technical institutes.

[21] *A Call for Action,* American Council on Education, Washington, 1954, p. 9.

CHAPTER 3

# Present Status

Curriculums of the technical institute type existed for more than a century in the United States before there was any attempt at comprehensive definition and survey of the field. The 1931 study of the SPEE identified thirty-two institutions offering daytime or evening courses within the scope of their technical institute definition.[1] These institutions listed a total of ninety-seven curriculums which could be classified into sixteen major fields.

## Enrollment trends since World War II

Since 1945 the annual surveys published in *Technical Education News* have provided a ready source of data about technical institutes.[2] The full-time enrollment, part-time enrollment, and total full- and part-time enrollments are shown in Table 2. Accurate data are not available for the prewar years, but at the time the first annual survey

[1] William E. Wickenden and Robert H. Spahr, *A Study of Technical Institutes,* Society for the Promotion of Engineering Education, Lancaster, Pa., 1931, pp. 40–45.

[2] Leo F. Smith, "Annual Survey of Technical Institutes, 1954–1955," *Tech. Educ. News,* July–August, 1955, p. 1.

was made in 1944–1945, those institutes responding indicated that the day enrollment in 1940–1941 totaled approximately 10,000.

A study of Table 2 reveals several interesting facts:

TABLE 2

ENROLLMENT TRENDS IN TECHNICAL INSTITUTES

| Year | Number of Institutes Reporting | Full-time Students | | | Part Time | Total Full and Part Time |
|---|---|---|---|---|---|---|
| | | Men | Women | Total | | |
| 1944–1945 | 44 | * | * | 8,721 | 10,154 | 18,875 |
| 1945–1946 | 50 | 9,936 | 841 | 10,777 | 7,879 | 18,656 |
| 1946–1947 | 77 | 27,771 | 1,359 | 29,130 | 20,305 | 49,435 |
| 1947–1948 | 82 | 29,784 | 1,143 | 30,927 | 16,714 | 47,641 |
| 1948–1949 | 81 | 31,616 | 1,710 | 33,326 | 19,531 | 52,857 |
| 1949–1950 | 66 | 29,444 | 2,229 | 31,673 | 20,073 | 51,746 |
| 1950–1951 | 66 | 22,125 | 2,220 | 24,345 | 22,096 | 46,441 |
| 1951–1952 | 64 | 17,209 | 2,422 | 19,631 | 26,786 | 46,417 |
| 1952–1953 | 67 | 16,213 | 2,627 | 18,840 | 33,897 | 52,737 |
| 1953–1954 | 62 | 18,700 | 2,827 | 21,527 | 29,410 | 50,937 |
| 1954–1955 | 69 | * | * | 26,766 | 33,981 | 60,747 |

* Data on the enrollment of men and women not collected separately.

1. The number of institutes reporting increased greatly from 1944–1945 to 1948–1949, decreased sharply in 1949–1950, and since then has continued at a relatively constant number. This rapid increase is accounted for in part by the

fact that during the first few years in which the surveys were made not all of the institutes were included which should have been. In addition, a number of new institutes were established following World War II. Some of these were proprietary institutes which opened in response to the demand for training veterans. Others were established as state institutions or as extension divisions of colleges and universities. For example, in 1946 New York State established five new Institutes of Applied Arts and Sciences. In 1945 Pennsylvania State University opened thirteen day and evening institutes throughout the State, and at about the same time Purdue University established four.

2. The sudden decrease in the number of institutes reporting in 1949–1950 is more apparent than real. In that year the enrollment from all the Penn State institutes was grouped together and included as one rather than thirteen, and the same was true for Purdue. By this time several of the proprietary institutes had also closed as the number of veterans seeking this type of training decreased.

3. The day enrollment of full-time students increased from a low of 8721 in 1944–1945 to a high of 33,326 in 1948–1949, and in 1954–1955 it was 26,766. This wide fluctuation in day enrollment might be attributed in part to the different number of institutes reporting. A study of twelve institutes that had responded to every one of the surveys, however, revealed the same trend. That is, the lowest enrollment was in 1944–1945, highest in 1948–1949, a steady decline to 1952–1953, and a rising trend since that time.

4. The part-time enrollment, which includes evening

and special students, has climbed almost steadily from 7879 in 1945–1946 to 33,981 in 1954–1955. This enrollment exceeded the regular day enrollment for the first time in 1951–1952 and has continued above since then. It would appear that technical institute educators are beginning to realize that the provision of evening and special courses for adults is one of the unique objectives for which the institutes are particularly well suited.

5. The institutes have enrolled men in much greater proportions than women. The percentage of women has ranged from a low of 3.8 per cent in 1947–1948 to a high of 13.9 per cent in 1952–1953 for all courses which have been reported in the annual surveys. An analysis of the enrollment of women in purely technological curriculums is considerably lower than these figures would indicate.

### The eleventh annual survey

The preceding paragraphs have dealt with the total number of institutes reporting and the enrollment trends in these institutions. The following paragraphs indicate the specific enrollment by types of institutes as of January, 1955.

Table 3 reveals that in the sixty-nine institutes reporting there were 26,766 regular day students, 33,981 part-time, and a grand total of 60,747. Column 1 of this table indicates the type of control under which these institutes operated. Twenty-two operated under state or municipal direction, twelve were privately endowed, fourteen were extension divisions of colleges and universities, nineteen were proprietary institutions, and two operated as YMCA schools. In addition, seven Canadian institutes reported day enrollment of 2648 regular day students, 8033 part-time students, and a total enrollment of 10,681. All of these Canadian institutes were under municipal or provincial control.

*Maritime academies and Federal schools*

When the first annual survey of technical institutes was made in 1944–1945, there were eight schools which fell in this category. Five of these were state maritime academies, two were U.S. Maritime Service Officers Schools, and one was the U.S. Merchant Marine Academy. The state maritime academies were located in California, Maine, Massachusetts, New York, and Pennsylvania. In June, 1947, the Pennsylvania State Legislature discontinued the maritime academy in that state. The other four academies have increased the length of their programs so that all graduates now receive the B.S. in Marine Engineering, and as a result these academies are no longer included in the annual surveys. In 1947–1948 the deputy supervisor of the U.S. Merchant Marine Corps asked that the Merchant Marine Academy no longer be included in the surveys.

The U.S. Maritime Service Officers Schools were discontinued as officers' schools in 1946 and a peacetime training program for merchant seamen inaugurated in 1947. By 1954 all the latter programs had been discontinued.

*State and municipal technical institutes*

These institutes range in size from 40 full-time day students at the Putnam (Conn.) Technical School to 2543 full-time day students at the New York City Community College of Applied Arts and Sciences in Brooklyn, as shown in Table 4. Although they range in geographical distribution from the Atlantic to the Pacific coasts, only three are located west of the Mississippi River. In 1954–1955 a total of 11,255 day students was reported by twenty-two institutes and 10,451 were enrolled part time, making a total day and part-time enrollment of 21,706. The wide variety of curriculums offered in these institutes will be explained in more detail in Chapter 4.

*Privately endowed institutes*

Table 5 lists an enrollment of 4624 regular day students in attendance at twelve institutes. In addition, 8503 part-time students were reported, making a grand total of 13,127 students.

*Extension divisions of colleges and universities*

In the responses received to the Eleventh Annual Survey, fourteen colleges and universities reported enrollments in courses offered in their extension and evening divisions as being technical institute in nature. Table 6 reveals an enrollment of 4608 day students, 11,319 part-time students, and a total of 15,927.

*Proprietary institutes*

Table 7 lists a regular day enrollment of 6153 in nineteen proprietary institutes, 2800 part-time students, and a total of 8953.

*YMCA schools*

For the past several years enrollments have been reported from two YMCA Schools only. For 1954–1955 the regular day enrollment was 126, with 908 part time, for a total of 1034. These figures are shown in Table 8.

*Canadian schools*

Seven Canadian institutes received a total of 2648 day students in 1954–1955, 8033 part-time students, and a total of 10,681. Enrollment by schools is listed in Table 9.

## Terminal education in junior colleges and community colleges

Dr. Jesse Bogue, Executive Secretary of the American Association of Junior Colleges (AAJC), in his comprehensive work on the community college, devotes a chapter to technical education and succinctly sums up the status as follows:[3]

> In attempts to meet the needs of employment at the intermediate level of occupations, sometimes called semiprofessional, community and junior colleges are giving a great deal of attention especially at the top-planning stages. Progress is being made, although it must be confessed that it is neither extensive nor rapid.

The annual surveys of technical institutes have made no attempt to include the enrollment in terminal education

[3] Jesse P. Bogue, *The Community College,* McGraw-Hill Book Company, Inc., New York, 1950, p. 189.

programs in junior colleges. This omission has been intentional, since the task of surveying approximately 600 junior colleges to determine the types of curriculums offered and the enrollment in these curriculums would be considerable. Ever since the Commission on Junior College Terminal Education was organized in 1939 to sponsor a nationwide study of terminal education in junior colleges, there has been considerable interest in this type of education. Accurate and up-to-date figures on the actual enrollment are, however, difficult to obtain.

In 1938–1939 Eells[4] reported an enrollment of 41,507 (34 per cent) students in terminal curriculums of the total of 121,573 reported by 426 institutions. Of these 35 per cent were enrolled in business curriculums, 16 per cent in public service, 15 per cent in general cultural, 11 per cent in engineering and technology, 8 per cent in fine arts, and 15 per cent in all other types.

Personal correspondence with Dr. C. C. Colvert, Director of Research for the AAJC, revealed that he had made a questionnaire survey in October, 1953, and found that approximately 114 junior colleges had "two- or three-year technical engineering programs." No data were given on enrollment in these programs.

A study made by Dr. Harold P. Rodes for the Office of the Relations with Schools of the University of California revealed an estimated technical institute enrollment of 6793 (11.7 per cent) of a total of 58,205 students en-

[4] Walter C. Eells, *Present Status of Junior College Terminal Education,* American Association of Junior Colleges, Washington, 1941, pp. 52–53.

rolled in full-time day programs in California junior colleges in the fall semester, 1950.[5]

It is interesting to note that the 11.7 per cent enrollment in technical institute curriculums revealed in Rodes's study compares very closely with the 11 per cent enrolled in engineering and technology curriculums found by Eells in 1938–1939.

**Summary**

Several conclusions may be drawn about the present status of technical institute education:

1. The number of institutes as reported in the annual surveys has increased from forty-four in 1944–1945 to sixty-nine in 1954–1955.
2. The number of full-time day students attending technical institutes has increased from 8721 in 1944–1945 to 26,766 in 1954–1955. This is an increase of 307 per cent.
3. The part-time enrollment, which includes evening and special students, has risen from 7879 in 1945–1946 to 33,981 in 1954–1955. This is an increase of 430 per cent.
4. Technical institute curriculums are offered by the following types of institutions: state or municipal, privately endowed, extension divisions of colleges and universities; proprietary institutions, and YMCA schools. When the surveys were originally initiated, technical institute curriculums were also offered by state maritime academies and Federal schools. The former have now length-

[5] Minutes of Advisory Committee on Technical Education in the Junior Colleges, December 15, 1950, Contra Costa Junior College, Richmond, Calif., Appendix B.

ened their programs and grant the baccalaureate degree, while the Federal schools offering technical institute curriculums have been closed.

5. There has been considerable interest in terminal education in community and junior colleges, and administrators of these institutions are giving considerable attention to the planning of these programs.

TABLE 3

ENROLLMENTS IN TECHNICAL INSTITUTES, 1954–55

| Type of Institution | Number of Schools | Enrollment 1954–1955 | | | Enrollment 1953–1954 | | |
|---|---|---|---|---|---|---|---|
| | | Full Time | Part Time | Total | Full Time | Part Time | Total |
| State and municipal.. | 22 | 11,255 | 10,451 | 21,706 | 9,903 | 7,913 | 17,816 |
| Privately endowed... | 12 | 4,624 | 8,503 | 13,127 | 2,780 | 7,798 | 10,578 |
| Extension divisions of colleges and universities. | 14 | 4,608 | 11,319 | 15,927 | 2,993 | 9,774 | 12,767 |
| Proprietary... | 19 | 6,153 | 2,800 | 8,953 | 5,800 | 3,421 | 9,221 |
| YMCA schools..... | 2 | 126 | 908 | 1,034 | 51 | 504 | 555 |
| Total.... | 69 | 26,766 | 33,981 | 60,747 | 21,527 | 29,410 | 50,937 |
| Canadian schools .... | 7 | 2,648 | 8,033 | 10,681 | 2,183 | 4,817 | 7,000 |

SOURCE: Leo F. Smith, "Annual Survey of Technical Institutes 1954–1955," *Tech. Educ. News*, July–August, 1955, p. 1.

## TABLE 4

STATE AND MUNICIPAL TECHNICAL INSTITUTES

| Name and Location | 1954–1955 Enrollment | | |
|---|---|---|---|
| | Full Time | Part Time | Total |
| Broome County Technical Institute, Binghamton, N.Y. | 287 | 223 | 510 |
| California State Polytechnic College, San Luis Obispo, Calif.* | 158 | ..... | 158 |
| Connecticut State Technical Institute, Hartford | 142 | 507 | 649 |
| Erie County Technical Institute, Buffalo, N.Y. | 790 | 1,168 | 1,958 |
| Fashion Institute of Technology, New York | 405 | 992 | 1,397 |
| Hudson Valley Technical Institute, Troy, N.Y. | 339 | 563 | 902 |
| Long Island Agricultural and Technical Institute, Farmingdale, N.Y. | 1,163 | 2,952 | 4,115 |
| Mohawk Valley Technical Institute, Utica, N.Y. | 257 | 325 | 582 |
| New Bedford Institute of Textiles and Technology, New Bedford, Mass. | 73 | 8 | 81 |
| New Hampshire Technical Institute, Manchester | 200 | 146 | 346 |
| New Hampshire Technical Institute, Portsmouth | 121 | 202 | 323 |
| NYC Community College of Applied Arts and Science, Brooklyn | 2,543 | 1,859 | 4,402 |
| NY State Agricultural and Technical Institute, Alfred | 1,135 | 264 | 1,399 |
| NY State Agricultural and Technical Institute, Canton | 377 | ..... | 377 |

* In addition, 2535 students are enrolled in four-year courses leading to B.S. degree.

TABLE 4 (*Continued*)

| Name and Location | 1954–1955 Enrollment | | |
|---|---|---|---|
| | Full Time | Part Time | Total |
| NY State Agricultural and Technical Institute, Delhi | 211 | 3 | 214 |
| NY State Agricultural and Technical Institute, Morrisville | 528 | ... | 528 |
| NY State Institute of Agriculture and Home Economics, Cobleskill | 281 | ... | 281 |
| North Dakota State School of Science, Wahpeton | 760 | 3 | 763 |
| Oregon Technical Institute, Oretech | 891 | 11 | 902 |
| Putnam Technical School, Putnam, Conn | 40 | 0 | 40 |
| School of Industrial Arts, Trenton, N.J | ... | 462 | 462 |
| Westchester Community College, White Plains, N.Y | 554 | 763 | 1,317 |
| Total | 11,255 | 10,451 | 21,706 |

SOURCE: Leo F. Smith, "Annual Survey of Technical Institutes 1954–1955," *Tech. Educ. News*, July–August, 1955, p. 1.

## Table 5

PRIVATELY ENDOWED TECHNICAL INSTITUTES

| Name and Location | 1954–1955 Enrollment | | |
|---|---|---|---|
| | Full Time | Part Time | Total |
| Alliance Technical Institute, Cambridge Springs, Pa. | 44 | ..... | 44 |
| Cogswell Polytechnical College, San Francisco | 79 | ..... | 79 |
| Franklin Technical Institute, Boston | 217 | 678 | 895 |
| Le Tourneau Technical Institute, Longview, Texas | 408 | 63 | 471 |
| Mechanics Institute, New York | ..... | 1,318 | 1,318 |
| Milwaukee School of Engineering, Milwaukee, Wis.* | 1,136 | ..... | 1,136 |
| Multnomah College—Technical Division, Portland, Ore | 208 | 107 | 315 |
| Ohio Mechanics Institute, Cincinnati, Ohio | 229 | 1,324 | 1,553 |
| Philadelphia Wireless Technical Institute, Philadelphia | 81 | 209 | 290 |
| Rochester Institute of Technology, Rochester, N.Y.† | 1,227 | 3,832 | 5,059 |
| Spring Garden Institute, Philadelphia | 315 | 972 | 1,287 |
| Wentworth Institute, Boston | 680 | ..... | 680 |
| Total | 4,624 | 8,503 | 13,127 |

* In addition, 251 students are enrolled in programs leading to B.S. degrees.

† In addition, 117 students are enrolled in programs leading to B.S. degrees.

Source: Leo F. Smith, "Annual Survey of Technical Institutes 1954–1955," *Tech. Educ. News*, July–August, 1955, p. 2.

TABLE 6

EXTENSION DIVISIONS OF COLLEGES AND UNIVERSITIES OFFERING TECHNICAL INSTITUTE COURSES

| Name and Location | 1954–1955 Enrollment | | |
|---|---|---|---|
| | Full Time | Part Time | Total |
| College of William and Mary—Technical Institute, Norfolk, Va. | 168 | 210 | 378 |
| Fenn College—Technical Institute, Cleveland, Ohio | ..... | 1,045 | 1,045 |
| Hillyer College—Ward School of Electronics, Hartford, Conn. | 226 | 192 | 418 |
| Lawrence Institute of Technology—Technical Institute Division, Detroit | ..... | 610 | 610 |
| Lowell Institute School, Cambridge, Mass. | ..... | 470 | 470 |
| Oklahoma A. and M. College—School of Technical Training, Stillwater | 420 | ..... | 420 |
| Pennsylvania State University Technical Institutes, University Park | 902 | 4,990 | 5,892 |
| Purdue University Technical Institutes, Lafayette, Ind. | 194 | 1,903 | 2,097 |
| Southern Technical Institute, Chamblee, Ga. | 601 | ..... | 601 |
| Temple University—Technical Institute and Community College, Philadelphia | 525 | 1,675 | 2,200 |
| University of Dayton—Technical Institute, Dayton, Ohio | 101 | 224 | 325 |
| University of Houston—College of Technology, Houston, Tex.* | 1,006 | ..... | 1,006 |
| Southern Illinois University, Carbondale | 405 | ..... | 405 |
| West Virginia Institute of Technology, Montgomery | 60 | ..... | 60 |
| Total | 4,608 | 11,319 | 15,927 |

* In addition, 503 students are enrolled in vocational courses.

SOURCE: Leo F. Smith, "Annual Survey of Technical Institutes 1954–1955," *Tech. Educ. News*, July–August, 1955, p. 2.

Table 7

PROPRIETARY TECHNICAL INSTITUTES

| Name and Location | 1954–1955 Enrollment | | |
|---|---|---|---|
| | Full Time | Part Time | Total |
| Academy of Aeronautics, New York | 559 | 313 | 872 |
| Acme School of Die Design Engineering, South Bend, Ind | 232 | 360 | 592 |
| Aeronautical University, Chicago | 155 | ... | 155 |
| American Television Institute of Technology, Chicago | 325 | 179 | 504 |
| Bowman Technical School, Lancaster, Pa | 80 | ... | 80 |
| Cal-Aero Technical Institute, Glendale, Calif.* | ... | ... | ... |
| Capitol Radio Engineering Institute, Washington | 310 | 280 | 590 |
| Central Technical Institute, Kansas City, Mo | 727 | 126 | 853 |
| Chicago Technical College, Chicago | 421 | 507 | 928 |
| Detroit Engineering Institute, Detroit | 55 | 22 | 77 |
| Electronics Institute, Detroit | 605 | 120 | 725 |
| Indianapolis Electronic School, Indianapolis | 78 | 131 | 209 |
| Industrial Trades Institute, Atlanta | ... | 14 | 14 |
| Lain Drafting College, Indianapolis | 90 | 64 | 154 |

* Has discontinued operations.

TABLE 7 (*Continued*)

| Name and Location | 1954–1955 Enrollment | | |
|---|---|---|---|
| | Full Time | Part Time | Total |
| New England Technical Institute, Providence, R.I., and Hartford, Conn. | 250 | 327 | 577 |
| Northrop Aeronautical Institute, Inglewood, Calif. | 885 | ... | 885 |
| Penn Technical Institute, Pittsburgh, Pa. | 197 | 189 | 386 |
| RCA Institutes, Inc., New York† | 493 | 168 | 661 |
| Spartan School of Aeronautics, Tulsa, Okla. | 355 | ... | 355 |
| Valparaiso Technical Institute, Valparaiso, Ind. | 336 | ... | 336 |
| Total | 6,153 | 2,800 | 8,953 |

† In addition, 835 full-time and 726 part-time students are enrolled in vocational courses in radio and television.

SOURCE: Leo F. Smith, "Annual Survey of Technical Institutes 1954–1955," *Tech. Educ. News*, July–August, 1955, p. 3.

TABLE 8

YMCA SCHOOLS OFFERING TECHNICAL INSTITUTE COURSES

| Name and Location | 1954–1955 Enrollment | | |
|---|---|---|---|
| | Full Time | Part Time | Total |
| Franklin University Technical Institute, Columbus, Ohio | 71 | 190 | 261 |
| Sinclair College, Dayton, Ohio | 55 | 718 | 773 |
| Total | 126 | 908 | 1,034 |

SOURCE: Leo F. Smith, "Annual Survey of Technical Institutes 1954–1955," *Tech. Educ. News*, July–August, 1955, p. 3.

TABLE 9

CANADIAN TECHNICAL INSTITUTES

| Name and Location | 1954–1955 Enrollment | | |
|---|---|---|---|
| | Full Time | Part Time | Total |
| Ecole Provinciale de Papeterie, Trois-Rivières, Que | 112 | ..... | 112 |
| Lakehead Technical Institute, Port Arthur, Ont | 28 | ..... | 28 |
| Montreal Technical School, Montreal, Que | 508 | 2,518 | 3,026 |
| Provincial Institute of Mining, Haileyburg, Ont | 98 | ..... | 98 |
| Provincial Institute of Textiles, Hamilton, Ont | 20 | 57 | 77 |
| Provincial Institute of Technology and Art, Calgary, Alta | 294 | ..... | 294 |
| Ryerson Institute of Technology, Toronto, Ont | 1,588 | 5,458 | 7,046 |
| Total | 2,648 | 8,033 | 10,681 |

SOURCE: Leo F. Smith, "Annual Survey of Technical Institutes 1954–1955," *Tech. Educ. News*, July–August, 1955, p. 3.

CHAPTER 4

# Curriculums Offered

In the previous chapter an analysis was made of the growth of technical institutes as indicated by the enrollments in the various institutions offering this type of education. This chapter will be devoted to a study of the following:

1. The number and types of curriculums offered.
2. The enrollment in these curriculums.
3. The number of graduates from the various curriculums.
4. The number of semester and contact hours devoted to courses in the basic sciences, technical specialties, administrative and managerial courses, and general education.

## Number and types of curriculums offered

Two statements have frequently been made about technical institutes which are worthy of study:

1. The curriculums in these institutes have developed in response to the need of a particular area or community.
2. There is a lack of agreement regarding the nomenclature concerning curriculums and graduates.

One of the best illustrations which could be offered of the truth of these statements is a study of the variety and types of curriculums to be found. In 1946 there was a total of 180 curriculums reported by seventy-seven institutes.[1] Of these, 138 were in engineering and technological fields, 16 in agriculture, 6 in graphic arts; 4 in home economics, 3 in health services, and 13 in miscellaneous areas. In the engineering and technological fields the curriculums were classified by the author under nineteen different titles ranging in content from aviation technology to textile technology.

In the eleventh annual survey of technical institutes[2] 347 currriculums were offered in the sixty-seven institutes reporting. Tables 10 and 11 list the numbers and types of curriculums offered by institutes under different types of control. Of these, 251 were in the technological area, while 96 were in areas other than technological. The technological curriculums were classified under thirty-three different titles as shown on Table 10. It is interesting to note that the 149 ECPD-accredited engineering schools reported a total of only twenty-one different engineering curriculums in October, 1952.[3]

The 96 nontechnological curriculums were reported as follows: 20 in agriculture, 31 in business, 11 in graphic

[1] Leo F. Smith, "Technical Institute Curriculums," *Tech. Educ. News,* October, 1946, pp. 1–5.

[2] Leo F. Smith, "Annual Survey of Technical Institutes 1954–1955," *Tech. Educ. News,* August, 1955, p. 1.

[3] Robert C. Story and Henry H. Armsby, "Engineering Enrollment and Degrees, 1952," *J. Engng. Educ.,* vol. 43, p. 5, February, 1953.

### Table 10

TYPES AND NUMBERS OF TECHNOLOGICAL CURRICULUMS OFFERED IN TECHNICAL INSTITUTES, 1954–1955

| Curriculum | State | Privately Endowed | Extension Divisions Colleges and Universities | Proprietary | YMCA Schools | Totals |
|---|---|---|---|---|---|---|
| Aeronautical technology | ... | ... | ... | ... | ... | 15 |
| Aircraft design | 1 | ... | ... | 2 | ... | *3* |
| Aircraft and engine maintenance | 1 | 1 | 2 | 4 | ... | *8* |
| Aircraft technology | ... | ... | ... | 3 | ... | *3* |
| Aircraft operations | 1 | ... | ... | ... | ... | *1* |
| Air conditioning, heating, and refrigeration | 5 | 2 | 5 | 1 | ... | 13 |
| Architectural, building construction, and civil technology | ... | ... | ... | ... | ... | 32 |
| Architectural | 2 | 2 | 2 | 2 | ... | *8* |
| Building construction | 8 | 3 | 4 | 1 | ... | *16* |
| Civil technology | 1 | ... | 1 | 1 | ... | *3* |
| Structural | 3 | 2 | ... | ... | ... | *5* |
| Automotive and diesel technology | 10 | 4 | 4 | ... | ... | 18 |
| Chemistry, industrial | 5 | 3 | 1 | ... | ... | 9 |
| Electrical technology | ... | ... | ... | ... | ... | 69 |
| Electrical construction and wiring | ... | 1 | ... | 1 | ... | *2* |
| Electrical technology | 14 | 8 | 8 | 1 | ... | *31* |

| | | | | | | |
|---|---|---|---|---|---|---|
| Industrial electronics | 2 | 4 | 2 | ... | ... | *8* |
| Radio and television | 5 | 4 | 8 | 10 | 1 | *28* |
| Fire protection technology | ... | ... | 1 | ... | ... | 1 |
| Food processing technology | 1 | ... | ... | ... | ... | 1 |
| Gas fuel technology | ... | ... | 1 | ... | ... | 1 |
| Industrial technology | 2 | 1 | 3 | 1 | 1 | 8 |
| Mechanical technology | ... | ... | ... | ... | ... | 67 |
| Drafting and machine design | 5 | 6 | 4 | 1 | 1 | *17* |
| Instrumentation | 3 | ... | 1 | ... | ... | *4* |
| Mechanical technology | 10 | 6 | 5 | 2 | ... | *23* |
| Steam diesel technology | ... | 3 | 2 | ... | ... | *5* |
| Tool and die making or design | 1 | 2 | ... | 1 | ... | *4* |
| Tool engineering technology | 1 | 2 | 1 | 2 | ... | *6* |
| Welding technology | 4 | 2 | 2 | ... | ... | *8* |
| Metallurgical technology | 1 | 1 | 1 | ... | ... | 3 |
| Optical technology | 1 | ... | ... | ... | ... | 1 |
| Textile technology | 1 | ... | ... | ... | ... | 1 |
| Miscellaneous courses | ... | ... | ... | ... | ... | 12 |
| Machine shop | 1 | 2 | 2 | ... | ... | *5* |
| Sheet metal | 1 | ... | ... | ... | ... | *1* |
| Watch and jewelry technology | 1 | ... | ... | 1 | ... | *2* |
| Other courses | 2 | 1 | 1 | ... | ... | *4* |
| Total | 93 | 60 | 61 | 34 | 3 | 251 |

arts, 14 in health services, 10 in home economics, and 10 miscellaneous. These data are shown in Table 11.

This survey showed a trend toward group differences among institutions with different means of financial support. Some of the highlights of these differences were:

1. All 20 of the agricultural curriculums were in the state agricultural and technical institutes. The state institutes also reported 93 curriculums in technological areas, 23 in business, 5 in graphic arts, 13 in health services, and 8 in home economics.
2. In the privately endowed institutes, 60 curriculums were in technological areas, 5 in graphic arts, 2 in business, 2 in home economics, and 2 miscellaneous.
3. Of the 70 curriculums offered by extension divisions of colleges and universities, 61 were technological in nature.
4. All but 1 of the 35 curriculums in proprietary institutes were in technological areas.

## Student enrollment in various curriculums

In the previous chapter the enrollment in technical institutes with various types of support was analyzed. It is also of interest to study the enrollment by various types of curriculums. Table 12 indicates this enrollment by individual institutes and curriculums as reported in the Eleventh Annual Survey. Of the 251 technological curriculums reported, sixty-nine (27 per cent) were in the electrical technology field (electrical construction and wiring, electrical technology, industrial electronics, radio, and television) with an enrollment of 8436 (42 per cent) students of the total of 20,015 reported. The sixty-seven mechanical technology curriculums were second in number and enrollment, with 4113 (20 per cent) students reported. Thirty-two architectural, building construction, and civil technology curriculums were reported with a total enrollment of 1656 students. Fifteen aeronautical technology, eighteen automotive and diesel technology, and thirteen air-conditioning, heating, and refrigeration curriculums were next in order with reported enrollments of 2128, 1407, and 865, respectively.

In the curriculums other than the technological, those in the business area were most popular, with thirty-one different curriculums and an enrollment of 2688 students, which was 40 per cent of the total of 6751, reported. Agriculture with twenty different curriculums, health service with fourteen, and graphic arts with eleven, with 1174, 982, and 863 students, respectively, were next in order. These data are shown in Table 13.

Appendix 3 analyzes the enrollment by curriculums and individual institutes still further, since the number of students enrolled in each institute and in each curriculum is shown. It is believed that this information should be of considerable value to guidance counselors and others interested in locating schools offering specific curriculums.

## Technical institute graduates

Although enrollment figures tell an important part of the story of technical institute education, these figures

## Table 11

**TYPES AND NUMBERS OF OTHER THAN TECHNOLOGICAL CURRICULUMS OFFERED IN TECHNICAL INSTITUTES, 1954–1955**

| Curriculum | State | Privately Endowed | Extension Divisions Colleges and Universities | Total |
|---|---|---|---|---|
| Agriculture | | | | 20 |
| Agricultural industries | 5 | ... | ... | *5* |
| Agricultural, general | 7 | ... | ... | *7* |
| Animal and poultry husbandry | 3 | ... | ... | *3* |
| Farm power machinery | 1 | ... | ... | *1* |
| Floriculture and horticulture | 4 | ... | ... | *4* |
| Business | | | | 31 |
| Business, general | 4 | 1 | 1 | *7** |
| Executive assisting | 3 | ... | ... | *3* |
| Hotel technology | 2 | ... | ... | *2* |
| Retail distribution | 2 | 1 | 1 | *4* |
| Sales, industrial | 2 | ... | ... | *2* |
| Secretarial | 4 | ... | 3 | *7* |
| Technical office assisting | 4 | ... | ... | *4* |
| Apparel technology | 1 | ... | ... | *1* |
| Textile design | 1 | ... | ... | *1* |
| Graphic arts | | | | 11 |
| Applied art and advertising | 4 | 1 | ... | *5* |
| Photography | ... | 2 | ... | *2* |
| Printing and publishing | 1 | 2 | 1 | *4* |

* Includes 1 course in a YMCA school.

TABLE 11 (*Continued*)

| Curriculum | State | Privately Endowed | Extension Divisions Colleges and Universities | Total |
|---|---|---|---|---|
| Health services | | | | 14 |
| Dental hygiene | 3 | ... | ... | *3* |
| Dental laboratory technology | 1 | ... | ... | *1* |
| Medical laboratory technology | 3 | ... | ... | *3* |
| Medical office assisting | 3 | ... | ... | *3* |
| Practical nursing | 3 | ... | 1 | *4* |
| Home economics | | | | 10 |
| Clothing and textiles | 1 | 1 | ... | *2* |
| Food administration | 7 | 1 | ... | *8* |
| Miscellaneous | 5 | 2 | 2 | 10† |
| Total | 74 | 11 | 9 | 96 |

† Includes 1 course in a proprietary institute.

TABLE 12

TECHNICAL INSTITUTE ENROLLMENT IN TECHNOLOGICAL CURRICULUMS AS OF JANUARY, 1955

| Curriculum | State and Municipal | Privately Endowed | Extension Divisions Colleges and Universities | Proprietary | YMCA Schools | Total |
|---|---|---|---|---|---|---|
| Aeronautical technology | 77 | 68 | 29 | 1954 | ... | 2128 |
| Aircraft design and drafting | *2* | .... | .... | *104* | ... | *106* |
| Aircraft and engine maintenance | *21* | *68* | *29* | *1236* | ... | *1354* |
| Aircraft technology | .... | .... | .... | *614* | ... | *614* |
| Aircraft operations | *54* | .... | .... | .... | ... | *54* |
| Air conditioning, heating, and refrigeration | 204 | 158 | 401 | 102 | ... | 865 |
| Architectural, building construction, and civil technology | 883 | 324 | 238 | 211 | ... | 1656 |
| Architectural | *12* | *133* | *19* | *132* | ... | *296* |
| Building construction | *520* | *160* | *182* | *29* | ... | *891* |
| Civil technology | *38* | .... | *37* | *50* | ... | *125* |
| Structural technology | *313* | *31* | .... | .... | ... | *344* |
| Automotive and diesel technology | 948 | 320 | 139 | .... | ... | 1407 |
| Chemistry, industrial | 352 | 88 | 6 | .... | ... | 446 |
| Electrical technology | 174 | 1532 | 1988 | 3106 | 65 | 8436 |
| Electrical construction and wiring | .... | *33* | .... | *2* | ... | *35* |
| Electrical technology | *1370* | *421* | *1040* | *85* | ... | *2916* |
| Industrial electronics | *61* | *571* | *103* | .... | ... | *735* |
| Radio and television | [illegible] | [illegible] | [illegible] | [illegible] | [illegible] | [illegible] |

| | | | | | | |
|---|---|---|---|---|---|---|
| Fire protection technology | .... | .... | 47 | .... | ... | 47 |
| Food processing technology | 104 | .... | .... | .... | ... | 104 |
| Gas fuel technology | .... | .... | 41 | .... | ... | 41 |
| Industrial technology | 75 | 24 | 71 | 8 | 31 | 209 |
| Mechanical technology | 1242 | 1084 | 1291 | 490 | 6 | 4113 |
| Drafting and machine design | *126* | *330* | *249* | *21* | *6* | *732* |
| Instrumentation | *76* | .... | *26* | .... | ... | *102* |
| Mechanical technology | *944* | *548* | *635* | *172* | ... | *2299* |
| Steam and diesel technology | .... | *62* | *331* | .... | ... | *393* |
| Tool engineering technology | *33* | *14* | *16* | *65* | ... | *128* |
| Tool and die making or design | *34* | *100* | .... | *232* | ... | *366* |
| Welding technology | *29* | *30* | *34* | .... | ... | *93* |
| Metallurgical technology | 75 | 4 | 5 | .... | ... | 84 |
| Optical technology | 50 | .... | .... | .... | ... | 50 |
| Textile technology | 23 | .... | .... | .... | ... | 23 |
| Miscellaneous courses | 81 | 149 | 96 | 80 | ... | 406 |
| Machine shop | *24* | *94* | *94* | .... | ... | *212* |
| Sheet metal | *17* | .... | .... | .... | ... | *17* |
| Watch and jewelry technology | *18* | .... | .... | *80* | ... | *98* |
| Other courses | *22* | *55* | *2* | .... | ... | *79* |
| Total | 5859 | 3751 | 4352 | 5951 | 102 | 20,015 |

TABLE 13

TECHNICAL INSTITUTE ENROLLMENT IN OTHER THAN TECHNOLOGICAL CURRICULUMS AS OF JANUARY, 1955

| Curriculum | State and Municipal | Privately Endowed | Extension Divisions Colleges and Universities | Total |
|---|---|---|---|---|
| Agricultural | 1174 | ... | ... | 1174 |
| Agricultural industries | *197* | ... | ... | *197* |
| Agriculture, general | *542* | ... | ... | *542* |
| Animal and poultry husbandry | *160* | ... | ... | *160* |
| Farm power machinery | *63* | ... | ... | *63* |
| Floriculture and horticulture | *212* | ... | ... | *212* |
| Business | 2186 | 294 | 184 | 2688* |
| Business, general | *340* | *145* | *47* | *556** |
| Executive assisting | *396* | ... | ... | *396* |
| Hotel technology | *241* | ... | ... | *241* |
| Retail distribution | *324* | *149* | *15* | *488* |
| Sales, industrial | *157* | ... | ... | *157* |
| Secretarial | *205* | ... | *122* | *327* |
| Technical office assisting | *182* | ... | ... | *182* |
| Apparel technology | *277* | ... | ... | *277* |
| Textile design | *64* | ... | ... | *64* |
| Graphic arts | 400 | 456 | 7 | 863 |
| Applied art and advertising | *356* | *85* | ... | *441* |
| Photography | .... | *167* | ... | *167* |
| Printing and publishing | *44* | *204* | 7 | *255* |

* Includes 24 students in YMCA schools.

TABLE 13 (*Continued*)

| Curriculum | State and Munici-pal | Pri-vately En-dowed | Exten-sion Divi-sions Colleges and Uni-versities | Total |
|---|---|---|---|---|
| Health services | 943 | ... | 39 | 982 |
| Dental hygiene | *346* | ... | ... | *346* |
| Dental laboratory technology | *123* | ... | ... | *123* |
| Medical laboratory technology | *241* | ... | ... | *241* |
| Medical office assisting | *171* | ... | ... | *171* |
| Practical nursing | *62* | ... | *39* | *101* |
| Home economics | 265 | 57 | ... | 322 |
| Clothing and textiles | *21* | *19* | ... | *40* |
| Food administration | *244* | *38* | ... | *282* |
| Miscellaneous | 428 | 66 | 26 | 722† |
| Total | 5396 | 873 | 256 | 6751 |

† Includes 202 students in proprietary institutes.

could be misleading without a consideration of the number of graduates. Tables 14 and 15 list the number of students graduating from technical institutes in 1954 as reported in the eleventh annual survey. These are tabulated according to the types of curriculums and schools, and the institutes were asked to report graduates from curriculums which were one year or more in length.

Table 14 lists a total of 6971 graduates from technological curriculums, which is an increase of 10.9 per cent from the 6207 reported in 1953. The 6207 graduates from technological curriculums in 1953 is slightly more than 25.8 per cent of the 24,164 students granted engineering degrees from all engineering colleges in the United States in 1953.[4] Most studies which have been made of the need for technicians indicate that a ratio of from three to five technicians per engineer would be desirable. If the lower of these two ratios is accepted, then industry would have needed more than 70,000 technical institute graduates in 1953, which contrasts with the 6207 graduates from technological curriculums during that year.

A study of the various fields of technology reveals that the largest number of graduates were from curriculums in electrical technology—a total of 2879. Mechanical technology graduates were second in numbers with 1447; aeronautical graduates ranked third with 761; and architectural, building construction, and civil technology ranked fourth with 547.

Table 15 indicates a total of 2161 graduates from other

[4] H. H. Armsby and W. A. Jaracz, "Engineering Enrollments and Degrees, 1953," *J. Engng. Educ.*, vol. 44, p. 5, February, 1954.

than technological curriculums, that is, agricultural, business, graphic arts, health services, home economics, and miscellaneous. This number, compared with the 1903 reported in 1953, represents an increase of 13.6 per cent.

The grand total of graduates from technical institutes in 1954 was 9132 as compared with 8110 in 1953—an increase of 12.6 per cent.

## Components of accredited curriculums

The establishment of accreditation procedures by ECPD[5] and the formation of the Technical Institute Division of the ASEE have led to considerable development as well as growth in stature of technical institute programs. For example, in the past there had been no organized or recognized group which could meet together to discuss common problems and formulate attacks upon research which needed to be done. The Technical Institute Division of the ASEE provided this opportunity and committees were appointed by this division to study common problems. The work of the Curriculum Development Committee under the leadership of Karl Werwath made an important contribution in this area. This committee gathered and interpreted data on the nature and amount of the various components of the accredited curriculums.[6]

[5] H. P. Hammond, "Accrediting Technical Institutes," *J. Engng. Educ.*, vol. 38, pp. 616–621, May, 1948.

[6] Carmine Master and Kenneth Hammond, *Quantitative Analysis of Subject Matter in Technical Institute Type Curricula as Accredited by Engineers' Council for Professional Development on November 1, 1949.* Unpublished thesis submitted to the Milwaukee School of Engineering, 1950.

TABLE 14

NUMBER OF TECHNICAL INSTITUTE GRADUATES FROM TECHNOLOGICAL CURRICULUMS
JANUARY 1, 1954, TO DECEMBER 31, 1954

| Curriculum | State and Municipal | Privately Endowed | Extension Divisions Colleges and Universities | Proprietary | YMCA Schools | Total |
|---|---|---|---|---|---|---|
| Aeronautical technology | 24 | 14 | 5 | 718 | ... | 761 |
| Aircraft design and drafting | ... | ... | ... | *32* | ... | *32* |
| Aircraft and engine maintenance | *10* | *14* | *5* | *564* | ... | *593* |
| Aircraft technology | ... | ... | ... | *122* | ... | *122* |
| Aircraft operations | *14* | ... | ... | .... | ... | *14* |
| Air conditioning, heating, and refrigeration | 43 | 72 | 78 | 58 | ... | 251 |
| Architectural, building construction, and civil technology | 251 | 105 | 109 | 82 | ... | 547 |
| Architectural drafting | *4* | *67* | *44* | *47* | ... | *162* |
| Building construction | *147* | *31* | *55* | *20* | ... | *253* |
| Civil technology | *12* | ... | *10* | *15* | ... | *37* |
| Structural technology | *88* | *7* | ... | .... | ... | *95* |
| Automotive and diesel technology | 196 | 159 | 29 | .... | ... | 384 |
| Chemistry, industrial | 108 | 9 | 1 | .... | ... | 118 |
| Electrical technology | 449 | 520 | 558 | 1310 | 42 | 2879 |
| Electrical construction and wiring | ... | ... | ... | *3* | ... | *3* |
| Electrical technology | *335* | *131* | *204* | *26* | ... | *696* |

| | | | | | | |
|---|---|---|---|---|---|---|
| Industrial electronics | *39* | *155* | *94* | *175* | ... | *463* |
| Radio and television | *75* | *234* | *260* | *1106* | *42* | *1717* |
| Fire protection technology | ... | ... | 10 | .... | ... | 10 |
| Food processing technology | 27 | ... | ... | .... | ... | 27 |
| Gas fuel technology | ... | ... | 23 | .... | ... | 23 |
| Industrial technology | 26 | ... | 116 | 5 | ... | 147 |
| Mechanical technology | 421 | 296 | 312 | 405 | 13 | 1447 |
| Drafting and machine design | *59* | *124* | *66* | *7* | *5* | *261* |
| Instrumentation | *31* | ... | *60* | .... | ... | *91* |
| Mechanical technology | *267* | *84* | *126* | *34* | *4* | *515* |
| Steam and diesel technology | ... | *20* | *15* | .... | ... | *35* |
| Tool and die making or design | *19* | *36* | *40* | *350* | ... | *445* |
| Tool engineering technology | *8* | *32* | *3* | *14* | *4* | *61* |
| Welding technology | *37* | ... | *2* | .... | ... | *39* |
| Metallurgical technology | 33 | ... | 40 | .... | ... | 73 |
| Optical technology | 13 | ... | ... | .... | ... | 13 |
| Textile technology | 6 | ... | ... | .... | ... | 6 |
| Miscellaneous courses | 16 | 100 | 115 | 54 | ... | 285 |
| Machine shop | *5* | *68* | *2* | .... | ... | *75* |
| Sheet metal | *5* | ... | ... | .... | ... | *5* |
| Watch and jewelry technology | *6* | ... | ... | *40* | ... | *46* |
| Other courses | ... | *32* | *113* | *14* | ... | *159* |
| Total | 1613 | 1275 | 1396 | 2632 | 55 | 6971 |

## Table 15

NUMBER OF TECHNICAL INSTITUTE GRADUATES FROM OTHER THAN TECHNOLOGICAL CURRICULUMS

JANUARY 1, 1954, TO DECEMBER 31, 1954

| Curriculum | State and Municipal | Privately Endowed | Extension Divisions Colleges and Universities | Total |
|---|---|---|---|---|
| Agricultural | 368 | ... | 40 | 408 |
| Agricultural industries | *72* | ... | *40* | *112* |
| Agriculture, general | *156* | ... | ... | *156* |
| Animal and poultry husbandry | *54* | ... | ... | *54* |
| Farm power machinery | *11* | ... | ... | *11* |
| Floriculture and horticulture | *75* | ... | ... | *75* |
| Business | 730 | 67 | 38 | 852* |
| Business, general | *112* | *30* | *22* | *181** |
| Executive assisting | *121* | ... | ... | *121* |
| Hotel technology | *57* | ... | ... | *57* |
| Retail distribution | *148* | *37* | *2* | *187* |
| Sales, industrial | *45* | ... | ... | *45* |
| Secretarial | *80* | ... | *14* | *94* |
| Technical office assisting | *31* | ... | ... | *31* |
| Apparel technology | *113* | ... | ... | *113* |
| Textile design | *23* | ... | ... | *23* |
| Graphic arts | 121 | 112 | ... | 233 |
| Applied art and advertising | *117* | *28* | ... | *145* |
| Photographic technology | ... | *29* | ... | *29* |
| Printing and publishing | *4* | *55* | ... | *59* |

* Includes 17 graduates of YMCA schools

TABLE 15 (*Continued*)

| Curriculum | State and Municipal | Privately Endowed | Extension Divisions Colleges and Universities | Total |
|---|---|---|---|---|
| Health services | 439 | ... | ... | 439 |
| Dental hygiene | *151* | ... | ... | *151* |
| Dental laboratory technology | *60* | ... | ... | *60* |
| Medical laboratory technology | *89* | ... | ... | *89* |
| Medical office assisting | *55* | ... | ... | *55* |
| Practical nursing | *84* | ... | ... | *84* |
| Home economics | 103 | 70 | ... | 173 |
| Clothing and textiles | ... | *62* | ... | *62* |
| Food administration | *103* | *8* | ... | *111* |
| Miscellaneous | 45 | 11 | ... | 56 |
| Total | 1806 | 260 | 78 | 2161 |

In this study the technical institute curriculums in nine areas of concentration were analyzed in terms of the following components:

1. Basic sciences (including mathematics, physics, chemistry, biology, etc.)
2. Technical specialties (theoretical and applied subjects in a major field such as radio, refrigeration, etc.)
3. Allied technical specialties (studies in subjects allied to the major technological specialties such as drafting, slide rule, etc.)
4. Administrative and managerial (includes cost controls, industrial organization, and labor relations, etc.)
5. General education (English, economics, psychology, etc.)

A quantitative analysis of these data is presented in Table 16, which shows the average number and per cent of contact hours devoted to each of the five components. For example, in the ten electronics, radio, and television curriculums studied, an average of 1730 contact hours (75 per cent of the total) was devoted to the special technical courses in that field, 116 hours (5 per cent) to courses in allied technical specialties, 347 hours (15 per cent) to basic sciences, 18 hours (1 per cent) to administrative and managerial, and 109 (4 per cent) to general education.

The average for all the fifty-two curriculums studied reveals that 53 per cent of the time is devoted to technical specialties, 14 per cent to allied technical specialties, 23 per cent to basic sciences, 4 per cent to administrative and managerial courses, and 6 per cent to general education.

The averages shown in Table 16 are derived from a

TABLE 16

AVERAGE NUMBER AND PER CENT OF CONTACT HOURS DEVOTED TO EACH COMPONENT

| Curricular Area | Number of Curriculums Included | Technical Specialty | | Allied Technical Specialty | | Basic Science | | Administrative & Managerial | | General Education | | Total | |
|---|---|---|---|---|---|---|---|---|---|---|---|---|---|
| | | No. | % | No. | % | No. | % | No. | % | No. | % | No. | % |
| Electronics, radio, and television | 10 | 1730 | 75 | 116 | 5 | 347 | 15 | 18 | 1 | 109 | 4 | 2320 | 100 |
| Air conditioning, heating, and refrigeration | 3 | 778 | 44 | 340 | 19 | 399 | 22 | 169 | 10 | 98 | 5 | 1784 | 100 |
| Architectural and building construction | 7 | 1020 | 55 | 274 | 15 | 352 | 19 | 79 | 4 | 121 | 7 | 1846 | 100 |
| Aeronautical maintenance and production | 7 | 1436 | 57 | 447 | 18 | 578 | 22 | 22 | 1 | 44 | 2 | 2527 | 100 |
| Mechanical technology | 8 | 787 | 47 | 139 | 8 | 524 | 32 | 90 | 6 | 125 | 7 | 1665 | 100 |
| Industrial electricity | 10 | 798 | 53 | 198 | 13 | 344 | 23 | 46 | 3 | 119 | 8 | 1505 | 100 |
| Steam, diesel, and automotive technology | 3 | 1098 | 47 | 492 | 21 | 588 | 25 | 114 | 5 | 60 | 2 | 2352 | 100 |
| Civil technology | 1 | 1012 | 51 | 319 | 16 | 418 | 21 | 110 | 5 | 132 | 7 | 1991 | 100 |
| Other | 3 | 892 | 47 | 176 | 9 | 608 | 32 | 72 | 4 | 148 | 8 | 1896 | 100 |
| Average for all curriculums | ... | 1061 | 53 | 278 | 14 | 462 | 23 | 80 | 4 | 106 | 6 | 1987 | 100 |

SOURCE: Adapted from Carmine Master and Kenneth Hammond, *Quantitative Analysis of Subject Matter in Technical Institute Type Curricula as Accredited by Engineers' Council for Professional Development on November 1, 1949*. Unpublished thesis submitted to the Milwaukee School of Engineering, 1950.

distribution of contact hours having considerable range and because of this should be interpreted with caution. Table 17 shows the average number of semester credit hours devoted to each of the five components. The average ranges from 62.0 in the ten electronics, radio, and television programs studied to 79.8 in the one civil technology program. The average number of semester hours required for all the fifty-two curriculums analyzed was 71.5.

Radha C. Das, while a graduate student at Cornell University, made a detailed study of the electrical curriculums offered in twenty-two technical institutes in northeastern United States.[7] Readers interested in curriculums in this field will find his study of value.

## General education in the technical institute curriculum

In former years technical institutes as a group devoted but meager time and attention to courses in the social sciences, English, communications, and the humanities. Paralleling the growth in interest on the part of engineering educators in the social-humanistic stem of the curriculum, technical institute educators have somewhat belatedly come to recognize the need for additional work in this area, and in 1953 a Committee on General Education of the Technical Institute Division of the ASEE was appointed.

At the 1954 annual meeting of this division of the ASEE,

[7] Radha C. Das, *Analysis of Electrical Curricula in Selected Technical Institutes,* Mimeographed Bulletin No. 2, New York State School of Industrial and Labor Relations, Cornell University, Ithaca, N.Y., 1949.

TABLE 17

AVERAGE NUMBER OF SEMESTER CREDIT HOURS DEVOTED TO EACH COMPONENT

| Curricular Area | Number of Curriculums Included | Technical Specialty | Allied Technical Specialty | Basic Science | Administrative and Managerial | General Education | Total |
|---|---|---|---|---|---|---|---|
| Electronics, radio, and television | 10 | 38.0 | 3.0 | 14.0 | 1.0 | 6.0 | 62.0 |
| Air conditioning, heating, and refrigeration | 3 | 27.4 | 10.9 | 17.5 | 9.3 | 5.3 | 70.4 |
| Architectural and building construction | 7 | 18.4 | 7.5 | 12.1 | 3.7 | 5.1 | 74.8 |
| Aeronautical maintenance and production | 7 | 34.4 | 13.0 | 22.2 | 0 | 5.6 | 75.2 |
| Mechanical technology | 8 | 28.4 | 5.5 | 26.8 | 6.3 | 8.9 | 75.8 |
| Industrial electricity | 10 | 29.4 | 5.6 | 19.6 | 2.7 | 9.3 | 66.7 |
| Steam, diesel, and automotive technology | 3 | 32.0 | 8.0 | 19.0 | 8.5 | 3.0 | 70.5 |
| Civil technology | 1 | 34.4 | 14.0 | 19.4 | 5.3 | 6.7 | 79.8 |
| Other | 3 | 26.0 | 7.2 | 21.7 | 4.4 | 8.7 | 68.1 |
| Average for all curriculums | ... | 29.8 | 8.3 | 19.2 | 4.6 | 6.5 | 71.5 |

SOURCE: Adapted from Carmine Master and Kenneth Hammond, *Quantitative Analysis of Subject Matter in Technical Institute Type Curricula as Accredited by Engineers' Council for Professional Development on November 1, 1949*. Unpublished thesis submitted to the Milwaukee School of Engineering, 1950.

Booher reported on a survey of general education in technical institutes. He studied the catalogues of forty-eight institutes and surveyed 249 curriculums and found, "The average time devoted to general education in all 249 curriculums was 9.6 per cent of the total time required to complete the courses, with the range extending from 0 to 35 per cent."[8] Booher also found that in the ECPD-accredited curriculums the average time allotted was 9.36 per cent, with a range from 0 to 23 per cent. In the non-ECPD-accredited curriculums an average of 5.51 per cent of the time was devoted to general education, with a range from 0 to 35 per cent. The eleven New York State Institutes were studied separately because they all grant the Associate in Applied Science degree, for which the State Education Department has established certain requirements in general education. In these eleven institutes he found that the average percentage of general education was 20.3, with a range from 15.5 to 32 per cent. Less general education is offered in proprietary institutes, and Foster[9] has explained the reasons with balance and clarity.

## Summary

The study of technical institute curriculums currently offered reveals the following:

[8] Edward E. Booher, "Survey of General Education in Technical Institutes," *Tech. Educ. News,* Special Issue, 1954, p. 6. Readers interested in the problem of general education in technical institutes are referred to the articles by Karl O. Werwath, C. L. Foster, Philip C. Martin, and Francis E. Almstead in this issue.

[9] C. L. Foster, "Nontax-supported Technical Institutes and General Education," *Tech. Educ. News,* Special Issue, 1954.

1. In 1954–1955 a total of 347 different curriculums was offered; of these 251 were in the technological area and 96 in areas other than technological.

2. The curriculums most frequently reported were those in electrical technology. Of the 251 technological curriculums, 27 per cent were in electrical technology with 42 per cent of the students.

3. In 1954 a total of 9132 students graduated from technical institute curriculums which were one year or more in length. Of these, 6971 graduated from technological curriculums and 2161 from other than technological.

4. A quantitative study of the nature and amounts of the various components of technical institute curriculums revealed 53 per cent of the contact hours were devoted to courses in the technical specialties, 14 per cent to allied technical specialties, 24 per cent to basic sciences, 6 per cent to general education, and 4 per cent to administrative and managerial courses.

CHAPTER 5

# Careers of Graduates

In previous chapters it has been pointed out that preparation for a clearly defined job or cluster of jobs is the common objective of all technical institutes. The extent to which institutes achieve this objective may be determined in a large measure by a study of what happens to the graduates. It is the purpose of this chapter to illustrate the following:

1. The types of positions held by graduates.
2. The progress which graduates make as they move from job to job.
3. The salary trends in relation to the number of years after graduation.
4. The success which graduates have when they transfer to traditional institutions to pursue work toward the baccalaureate degree.

## Types of positions held

Prospective applicants to technical institutes, high school guidance counselors, teachers, and parents frequently ask, "What kind or types of positions do technical institute graduates obtain?" Perhaps the best way to answer this is to study the positions actually held by graduates of several different institutes.

In the questionnaire survey made by the authors in 1954 one question asked was:

> Have you made any studies of your graduates which would indicate:
> (*a*) Job titles upon graduation
> (*b*) Job titles 1, 3, 5, or more years after graduation
> (*c*) The percentages employed in supervision, sales, skilled jobs, drafting and design, industrial engineering, professional engineering jobs, teaching, etc.

More than 70 per cent of the forty institutes replying stated that they had made such studies, but in many instances these were not recent or the material had not been organized in the fashion called for. Several replies, however, were very complete and indicated that these institutes were doing a careful and painstaking job in order to determine the types of positions their graduates were occupying. In the following pages the results of studies of graduates from several institutes will be presented.

*Long Island Agricultural and Technical Institute*

This institute at Farmingdale, Long Island, N.Y., has utilized several interesting techniques to evaluate its programs. For example, the writers found in their 1954 questionnaire survey that

> All graduates are required to submit evidence of six months of satisfactory work experience in their field before

their degree is granted. This includes periodic written reports from the graduate concerning his duties, an interview by a faculty member with the employer and a visitation of the graduate on his job. Both the graduate and employer are interrogated as to the value of and omissions in the curriculum content in an effort to continually improve the program. . . . While job titles are available for all graduates they have not been summarized or broken down into categories except by certain departments for special studies. We do determine, however, that jobs fit our "cluster" or perhaps even suggest an addition to the "cluster." Our studies show that over eighty percent of the graduates are employed as technicians in the general field for which they were trained.

A study made in December, 1952, of the class which had graduated in June, 1952, revealed the typical initial job placements shown in Table 18.

*Oregon Technical Institute*

In a placement study of the class of June, 1952, this institute reported that of 169 students responding to the survey 144 (85.0 per cent) were employed in the occupation for which trained, 10 (6.0 per cent) were working in other occupations, 9 (5.4 per cent) were continuing studies, 5 (3.0 per cent) were in the armed services, and 1 (0.6 per cent) was an instructor.

*Alliance Technical Institute*

The Alliance Technical Institute, which is affiliated with Alliance College (a privately endowed college sup-

Table 18

INITIAL JOB PLACEMENTS, LONG ISLAND AGRICULTURAL AND TECHNICAL INSTITUTE

| Curriculum | Job title |
| --- | --- |
| Automotive and diesel technology | Junior draftsman |
| | Tester, gas turbine division |
| | Mechanic |
| Building construction | Transitman |
| | Engineering aide |
| | Building inspector |
| | Estimator |
| Electrical equipment and industrial electronics | Technician trainee |
| | Mechanical and electrical tester |
| | Electrical fixture calibrator |
| | Layout man |
| Industrial chemistry | Junior chemist |
| | Junior chemist and pilot-plant operator |
| | Control chemist |
| | Junior chemist, analysis of metals |
| Mechanical technology | Detailer |
| | Tool designer |
| | Test technician trainee |
| | Junior methods man |
| | Research technician |

ported by the Polish National Alliance), reported the following approximate placement of their graduates:

| | Per cent |
|---|---|
| Skilled jobs | 50 |
| Drafting and design | 35 |
| Further study after graduation to engineering and professional status | 10 |
| Teaching | 5 |

*Rochester Institute of Technology*

In a study made in 1953 of 934 men who had graduated from the Mechanical Department between the years 1926 and 1952, it was found that they were in the positions shown in Table 19.

TABLE 19

POSITIONS OF GRADUATES OF ROCHESTER INSTITUTE OF TECHNOLOGY, 1926–1952

| | Per cent |
|---|---|
| Engineering | 18 |
| Design engineer, process engineer, mechanical engineer, tool engineer, project engineer, production engineer, chief engineer, experimental engineer | |
| Precision machining | 13 |
| Instrument maker, machinist, toolmaker, tool- and diemaker, screw machine setup man, mechanic | |
| Supervision and managerial | 10 |
| Foreman, partner or co-owner, supervisor, general supervisor, president, assistant foreman, superintendent, vice-president, production manager | |

TABLE 19 (*Continued*)

| | Per cent |
|---|---|
| Drafting | 9 |
| Draftsman, layout draftsman, detail draftsman, design draftsman, engineering draftsman, chief draftsman | |
| Design | 8 |
| Tool designer, product designer, machine designer, industrial designer | |
| Sales and service | 4 |
| Sales engineer, sales representative, sales and service | |
| Industrial engineering | 4 |
| Inspector, methods engineer, time-study engineer, industrial engineer, expeditor, materials control, standards | |
| Power operation | 3 |
| Staff engineer, power clerk, power operator, power plant maintenance, gauge calibrator, instrument repairman, laboratory assistant | |
| Miscellaneous technical positions | 3 |
| Military service | 6 |
| Teaching, students, self-employed | 5 |
| Out of field | 2 |
| Deceased | 3 |
| No recent information | 12 |

### *The Pennsylvania State University Technical Institutes*

Since the close of World War II, Penn State has operated several day technical institutes throughout the state of Pennsylvania which have offered programs one year in length. In 1953 these institutions lengthened their programs to two years. Table 20 gives the results of a study made in 1952 by Floyd B. Fischer of the graduates, from 1948 to 1951 inclusive, of the one-year curriculums in building construction, industrial electricity, and mechanical and production tool design (1951 also included business administration graduates).

TABLE 20

STUDY OF GRADUATES OF THE PENNSYLVANIA STATE UNIVERSITY TECHNICAL INSTITUTES

| | |
|---|---|
| Total number of graduates | 749 |
| Total number of graduates reporting | 684 |
| Percentage reporting on survey | 91.3 |
| Percentage unemployed | 10.4 |
| Percentage in armed services | 4.8 |
| Percentage in college or other schools | 11.1 |
| Percentage working directly in field of training | 59.1 |
| Percentage working in other fields | 14.6 |
| Monthly salary range (of those reporting) | $100–$550 |
| Average starting salary per month (of those reporting) | $205 |

Several of the typical jobs held by graduates six to twelve months after graduation from three curriculums are listed in Table 21.

*Purdue University Division of Technical Institutes*

Purdue University Division of Technical Institutes made a study of the initial job placement of the graduates

Table 21

JOB PLACEMENTS, PENN STATE TECHNICAL INSTITUTES

| Curriculum | Job title |
| --- | --- |
| Building construction | Architectural draftsman |
| | Surveyor |
| | Surveyor aide |
| | Own contracting business |
| | Construction apprentice |
| | Engineering aide |
| | Structural draftsman |
| | Construction estimator |
| | Cost analyst |
| | Rodman |
| Industrial electricity | Television sales |
| | Technical trainee |
| | Television technician |
| | Electrical mechanic |
| | Tube tester, electrical |
| | Draftsman, electrical |
| | Quality control, electrical |
| | Assistant buyer, electrical plant |
| | Laboratory technician |
| | Production electrician |
| Mechanical and production tool design | Draftsman |
| | Detailer |
| | Turret lathe operator |
| | Design draftsman |
| | Sales engineer |
| | Junior tool designer |
| | Rodman |
| | Engineering aide |
| | Engineering technician |
| | Laboratory technician |

of the class of 1954 and representative job titles are reported in Table 22.

TABLE 22

INITIAL JOB PLACEMENTS, PURDUE UNIVERSITY DIVISION OF TECHNICAL INSTITUTES

| Curriculum | Job title |
|---|---|
| Building construction.... | Real estate broker |
| | Engineer |
| | Draftsman |
| | Truck driver |
| | Junior field engineer |
| Electrical technology.... | Instrumental repair |
| | Relief foreman |
| | Radio repair |
| | Instrument repairman |
| | Gang leader (maintenance mechanic) |
| Industrial technology.... | Self-employed |
| | Foreman |
| | Experimental boring-mill operator |
| | Salesman |
| | Quality control |

The total number of graduates from this class was 52 and the average salary earned by 34 reporting this item was $375 per month.

*The Community College and Technical Institute of Temple University*

The Technical Institute of Temple University recently conducted a survey of more than 700 graduates of its full-time radio and television courses to ascertain the nature of employment and types of positions held by them in industry. The following summary indicates the types of employment which these men had entered:

Research positions absorbed 32 per cent of the graduates. They went into positions in the laboratories of television and electronic manufacturers, and some hold technicians' positions with manufacturers of electronic calculators.

Another large group—representing 18 per cent—entered the radio and television servicing field. Some of them have obtained positions as service managers for the largest television servicing organizations in the country. Others are serving as assistant managers and general service technicians in this field, with companies of varied sizes.

The survey showed that radio stations, including AM and FM, and television stations in the eastern section of the United States hired 17 per cent of the graduates for positions as station engineers, transmitter operators, and general technicians. As to the types of stations which hired the graduates, it was found that 80 per cent could be classified as large stations, both as to power and listening audience.

A recent change of the employment picture brought about by the mobilization effort has created positions for electronic instructors, radar technicians, and technical writers. Seventeen per cent of the graduates have been employed in one of these three categories.

The tabulation showed that 7 per cent are self-employed, operating their own radio and television service organizations or stores, and are doing remarkably well financially.

Of 700 students surveyed, 9 per cent are in the armed services, are attending college, or failed to answer.

*The Milwaukee School of Engineering*

A five-year placement report just issued by the Milwaukee School of Engineering reveals some interesting information concerning the first job placement of men who had graduated from the radio-television technology and the air conditioning technology curriculums between December, 1948, and December, 1953.[2]

Of 260 graduates from the radio-television curriculum, 228 were placed in work directly related to their major field of study. The remaining 32 graduates entered the armed forces, went on for further study, or were absorbed in other ways. Some of the occupational titles most frequently given to these men on their first jobs were assembly technician, control room operator, development technician, draftsman, electronic technician, field service representative, installation supervisor, instrument mechanic, laboratory technician, owner of business, production technician, research technician, sales representative, and service man.

Of a total of 370 graduates from the air conditioning technology curriculum, 335 were working in their major field of study. Some of the first job titles reported by these men were design technician, draftsman, engineer's assistant, field service representative, general manager, inspector, installation supervisor, layout and estimating technician, plant superintendent, production superintendent, sales estimator, sales representative, service manager, and service specialist.

[2] "Five-year Placement Report Issue," *Milwaukee School of Engineering Bulletin,* vol. 6, no. 17, October, 1954.

## Job progression

It has already been indicated that training for a cluster of jobs is the common objective of all technical institutes. The concept of "job clusters" was developed at the Rochester Institute of Technology to indicate the number of related jobs to which graduates from a technical curriculum might go. In the original studies which were made, an analysis of the activities performed by workers in industry provided the initial basis for grouping these jobs into job charts. All of the jobs which required basically the same education were grouped into a job cluster or job chart. Table 23, the job chart for a machine designer, indicates the training, basic intermediate, and basic jobs and the supplementary and related jobs in this field.

TABLE 23

JOB CHART FOR MACHINE DESIGNER

| *Basic Job* | *Supplementary Jobs* | *Related Jobs* |
|---|---|---|
| Machine designer | Chief of standards | Chief engineer |
| | Chief draftsman | Catalogue and instruction book illustrator |
| | Tool designer | Calculator |
| | Technical supervisor | Chief of stockroom |
| *Basic Intermediate Jobs* | *Supplementary Intermediate Jobs* | Technical salesman |
| | | Field engineer |
| Checker | Inspector | Product engineer |
| Layout man | Technical correspondent | |
| Detailer | Order clerk | |

*Training Jobs*

| | |
|---|---|
| Stock chaser | Card system clerk |
| Assembler | Tracing file clerk |
| Assistant inspector | Tracer |
| Machine tool operator | Blueprint boy |
| Librarian | Errand boy |

Reading from the bottom of Table 23, there are listed the jobs which the Institute cooperative students usually hold. After a number of years of school and job training and after demonstrating their ability, graduates may advance to one of the intermediate jobs and within a number of years of additional experience they may advance to the basic job. The requirements for the supplementary and related jobs are similar to those for the basic job, and depending upon the employment opportunities and the interests and abilities of the graduates, they may progress to positions in these areas.

This chart was based upon a study of the available jobs in western New York. The selection of the jobs in each of the categories was determined by the amount of education and experience required. From periodic follow-up studies which have been made of graduates, these job charts have been altered and refined.

The New York State institutes have also adapted the job chart idea, and the Long Island Agricultural and Technical Institute at Farmingdale has published an interesting pamphlet[3] which gives illustrations of the types of progress made by several of their graduates of the class of 1948.

Despite their success in finding suitable employment, technical institute graduates have lacked uniform titles and credentials which would clearly identify their educational background. In studying this problem a com-

[3] *1953 Report on Placement and Progress of Graduates: Industrial Technical Division,* Long Island Agricultural and Technical Institute, Farmingdale, New York, 1953.

TABLE 24

JOB PROGRESS OF GRADUATES

| Curriculum | Initial job placement—1948 | 1953 job placement |
|---|---|---|
| Building construction | Rodman | Chief engineer |
| Aircraft operations | Operations attendant | Chief aircraft dispatcher |
| Industrial chemistry | Junior chemist | Head, Milium investigation |
| Industrial instrumentation | Technician | Junior instrument engineer |
| Mechanical technology | Draftsman | Tool designer |
| Radio communications | Production technician | Production supervisor |
| Refrigeration, heating, and air conditioning | Assistant engineer | Design engineer |

SOURCE: *1953 Report on Placement and Progress of Graduates: Industrial Technical Division*, Long Island Agricultural and Technical Institute, Farmingdale, New York, 1953.

mittee of the Technical Institute Division of the ASEE surveyed 304 firms and agencies employing more than 7,000 technical institute graduates. The distribution of titles is shown in Table 25.

In the interest of clarity and public understanding, the 1952 meeting of the Technical Institute Division passed a resolution urging members of the ASEE to refer to graduates of technical institutes as engineering technicians. The associate degree was designated as an appropriate title of accomplishment for graduates of a technical institute program.

TABLE 25

JOB TITLES OF GRADUATES

| Title | Number | Title | Number |
|---|---|---|---|
| Associate | 1 | Technician | 68 |
| Associate in engineering | 1 | Technical aide | 5 |
| Engineering aide | 20 | Technical assistant | 14 |
| Engineering assistant | 28 | Laboratory technician | 32 |
| Engineering associate | 2 | Other technical | 20 |
| Other engineering | 25 | Various supervisory titles | 53 |

SOURCE: R. Warren Marsh, report presented at the annual meeting of the ASEE, East Lansing, Michigan, June, 1951.

## Salary trends

Few accurate data are available regarding the salary trends of technical institute graduates, and the authors made no effort to collect such information. Several institutes, however, did report the results of studies which they had made and these are summarized below. It should be kept in mind that these studies were made at somewhat different dates and under somewhat different conditions. The numbers included in some cases are not great. Despite all of these limitations, it is believed that the data shown in Table 26 are of interest.

## Transfer problems

Although the primary objective of all technical institutes is to prepare graduates for a cluster of jobs immediately upon graduation, a number of graduates continue their work toward the baccalaureate degree. The SPEE study outlined some of the difficulties which graduates of

TABLE 26

AVERAGE MONTHLY SALARIES OF TECHNICAL INSTITUTE GRADUATES

(Figures in parentheses indicate number of graduates reporting salaries)

| Institute* | Number of Years since Class Graduated | | | | | | Time of Study |
|---|---|---|---|---|---|---|---|
| | 1 | 2 | 3 | 4 | 5 | 6 | |
| A | $344 (40) | 393 (30) | 396 (30) | 432 (33) | 460 (10) | ... | June, 1954 |
| B | 300 (19) | 346 (18) | 353 (20) | 346 (18) | 442 (25) | 440 (8) | April, 1954 |
| C | 290 (202) | 303 (200) | 338 (200) | 364 (?) | 390 (150) | ... | December, 1952 |
| D | 348 (33) | 318 (38) | 352 (31) | 373 (44) | ... | ... | Spring, 1952 |

* All the institutes reporting are publicly supported: A is in the South, B in New England, C in the Middle Atlantic states, and D is in the Middle West.

these institutions would encounter if they desired to transfer to engineering colleges.[4]

The colleges will not contend that the quality of the instruction at the institutes, in many cases, has been inferior;

[4] William E. Wickenden and Robert H. Spahr, *A Study of Technical Institutes,* Society for the Promotion of Engineering Education, Lancaster, Pa., 1931, p. 102.

> on the contrary, in some instances, the practice, laboratory, and shop work are more complete and thorough, and are done with superior equipment than is parallel work in most of the engineering colleges. Thus, the graduates from certain technical institutes experience little difficulty in obtaining credit in the leading engineering colleges for shop and laboratory. . . . The trouble arises in the "theoretical" courses which, by intention, have been different in content. For example, in most cases these technical institute men have neither had the amount nor the kind of mathematics for which the college will allow any considerable credit, regardless of how purposeful or useful the content or how thorough the instruction has been. The college faculty further insists that this mathematics is often neither of an adequate amount nor of the right type to help the student to pursue successfully certain more advanced engineering subjects.

While these objections on the part of traditional four-year institutions are undoubtedly partially justified, there are at least two studies which indicate that the better technical institute graduates can transfer to four-year institutions and compete successfully.

In 1951, in a research project sponsored by the State University of New York, Paul M. Williams, under the supervision of Philip A. Cowen, made a study of the 8784 graduates for the years 1947 through 1950 of the ten New York State technical institutes and the Rochester Institute of Technology. The author of this unpublished study was interested in finding answers to several problems:

1. What percentage of institute graduates transfer to college?

2. To what extent is credit transferable from a two-year course to a college course?

3. What adjustments may be necessary in transferring from a two-year program to a four-year program?

4. What factors affected the student's decision to continue his education beyond the two-year course?

5. Do graduates of two-year programs have a satisfactory understanding of college work, as reflected by college grades?

6. What adjustments or revisions in the two-year program would benefit those transferring to college?

In pursuing his research, Williams obtained the names and certain personal data from all the institutes of those graduates who had transferred to college. He then sent a questionnaire to the colleges to ascertain the progress which these students had made. In addition, he sent a questionnaire to the individual students to determine reasons for transfer, problems encountered, and credit received.

Williams found that of the 8784 graduates, 268 (3 per cent) had transferred to college. He comments as follows about this:

> Even though the New York State Institute program is terminal, about 3 per cent of the graduates do transfer to a four-year college. Although not a major problem to either the institute or the receiving college, this is a very serious problem to the individual students concerned.

This study also revealed that New York State Institute graduates received about one year of credit for their two year institute courses. The graduates of the Rochester Institute of Technology, where the program was full time during the first school year and cooperative during the second and third, received a little more than three semesters of credit.

The success which these students had in college is also pointed out by Williams:

> The replies of college officials who have observed institute graduates leads one to conclude that students desiring to transfer to college are a far better "college risk" than the average college freshman. Although it is fairly obvious that this group of institute graduates desiring to transfer to college is a more selective aggregation than a similar group of beginning freshmen, college officials sometimes fail to take cognizance of this fact.

The summary paragraph of this report is also of interest:

> If this study had accomplished nothing else it has brought to light students' reactions to a problem complicated by the intricacies of credit bookkeeping, subject evaluation, differences between practical and theoretical instruction, lack of understanding of the institute program, and the somewhat superior attitude taken toward non-[baccalaureate] degree granting institutions.

The other study, which pertains to the success of technical institute graduates, was made by the authors of the Rochester Institute of Technology graduates who had transferred to four-year colleges. In the fall of 1953, the department heads were asked to list a sampling of their graduates from 1942 through 1950 who had transferred to college and who had completed the work for their baccalaureate degree. The college registrars were then contacted and official transcripts obtained. It was discovered that the 31 graduates from the chemistry, electrical, and mechanical departments whose names were furnished had received credit ranging from 27 to 94 semester hours, with an average of 61. They had also made a grade point average of 2.82 (where A is equal to 4 grade points; B, 3; C, 2; etc.). Of the 31 students, 23 received degrees in engineering, and the remainder received degrees in the physical sciences. All the engineering curriculums represented in this study were ECPD-accredited. As a result of this study, the authors conclude[5]

> 1. That some engineering colleges grant substantial amounts of transfer credit to qualified technical institute graduates.
> 2. That this transfer credit is justified in terms of the subsequent success of those transfer students in the engineering colleges.

## Summary

Studies which have been made of technical institute graduates reveal the following:

1. An unusually high percentage find employment in the occupational field for which they were prepared.

[5] Leo F. Smith and Laurence Lipsett, "Can Technical Institute Graduates Succeed in Engineering Colleges?" *J. Engng. Educ.*, vol. 44, pp. 642–643, June, 1954.

2. A large percentage hold technical jobs on the engineering team.

3. Many advance to positions of supervisory responsibility.

4. A substantial number advance to full-fledged engineering responsibilities.

5. A small percentage transfer successfully to traditional engineering colleges and complete work for the B.S. degree.

Despite all the foregoing positive data, technical institute graduates have been handicapped by the lack of uniform titles and credentials which would clearly identify their educational background.

# PART TWO

## Organizing and Administering Technical Institute Programs

CHAPTER 6

# Determining Objectives

As technical institutes have evolved distinctive patterns of education, they have found that the most effective programs have been established as a result of several definite steps, which are listed below. It is undoubtedly true that not all technical institutes have utilized such a list, and probably no one institute has thoroughly completed all of these steps every time a new curriculum has been initiated. Nevertheless, any professional evaluation of a technical institute curriculum would consider the extent to which the institute had carried out these basic steps, which are:

1. Determine the broad objectives of the institution.
2. Survey the demand for one or more curriculums on the part of industry and potential students.
3. Select a curricular area which is appropriate in terms of demand, objectives, and institutional facilities.
4. Study job requirements in the occupational field selected.
5. Allocate each of the required knowledges, skills, and understandings to a course of instruction.
6. Determine type and amount of general education.

7. Plan a balanced and integrated program of study.

The chapters that follow are devoted to a discussion of the problems and techniques involved in each of these steps, while the present chapter will discuss in particular the method of determining technical institute objectives.

**What are objectives?**

Every educational institution has originated to serve some purpose or need. Out of this purpose or need grow educational objectives. Our elementary schools have as their purposes the development in each child of some degree of competence in the use of the English language in written and spoken form, the inculcation of the rudiments of arithmetic, and the socialization of each individual so that he or she will be able to work and play with other children. Our secondary schools have changed over the past several decades from being primarily preparatory schools for college to the point where most of them now have as their purposes the adjustment of young people to work, to home and family living, and to citizenship. The objectives of the universities of our country have been to prepare young men and women for the professions, to disseminate knowledge, and to push back the frontiers of knowledge by carrying on research.

Dr. W. W. Charters, in writing about the formulation of technical institutes' objectives more than two decades ago, made the following discerning statement:[1] "The objectives of an educational institution are the product of

[1] W. W. Charters, "Selecting Institutional Objectives," *Personnel J.*, vol. 7, p. 7, June, 1933.

three factors—social needs, student interests, and institutional facilities."

The principal social need which the technical institute attempts to fill is the need of industry for well-qualified employees in certain technical occupations. Preparation for these occupations fulfills equally important needs on the part of students who are interested in the duties of the occupation as well as its financial rewards, advancement, security, and social status. The facilities which the institute has, or is able to obtain, determine the particular occupations which will be served.

The nature of technical institutes makes it possible to define their objectives, or goals, or purposes, with greater clarity than is found in many other educational institutions. Briefly stated, the primary objective of technical institutes is to provide education which will qualify graduates for a series or cluster of related jobs within an occupational field.

In summary, the answer to the question, "What are objectives?" might be stated as follows: Educational objectives are the changes in students it is hoped will take place as a result of their enrollment in a certain course, curriculum, or school. These may be evidenced in the difference between measurements or observations made at entrance and at the time of completion of an educational program.

### Special objectives of technical institutes

All higher institutions in the United States, including technical institutes, have as one of their major objectives the preparation of students for effective and satisfying participation in a democratic and technological society. In addition to this broad objective, technical institutes have several objectives which they are particularly well-suited to achieve, the most important of which are as follows:

1. To prepare graduates for occupational competence in a clearly identified technological occupation or cluster of jobs. This objective has been, and continues to be, the central goal of technical institutes.

2. To serve the needs of industry for technical personnel within a geographical area, such as a city, region, or state. This is illustrated in New York State, where the State University established a series of technical institutes as a result of a statewide survey of industry.[2]

3. To provide instruction in the technology of specific industries. This objective appears to be peculiarly well-suited to technical institutes, and some outstanding programs have been developed. Southern Technical Institute has developed a program in gas technology which is unique in this country. The food technology curriculum at the New York State Agricultural and Technical Institute at Morrisville, the fire protection curriculum at the School of Technical Training of Oklahoma A. and M., and the photographic technology and screw machine technology curriculums at the Rochester Institute of Tech-

[2] J. Cayce Morrison, chairman, *A Guide to the Development of Programs for the Institutes of Applied Arts and Sciences,* The University of the State of New York, Albany, 1946.

nology are examples of highly specialized curriculums designed to meet the needs of specific industries.

4. To serve technical education needs of employed adults. While such courses have been offered over a long period of time by evening high schools and by extension divisions of colleges and universities, technical institutes are particularly well adapted for providing evening courses in certain technical fields, such as drafting, machine tool utilization, and technical mathematics.

## Special factors affecting objectives

There are various factors which cannot in themselves be considered objectives, but which do play an important part in determining the type of program offered by an institute. The most important of these are:

1. The emphasis which the institute administration places upon general education. In the past, concentration on occupational objectives led some technical institutes to omit entirely courses offered in English, the social sciences, and the humanities, or at least to reduce their number to a minimum. The rationale for this omission was that in the length of time available in most technical institute curriculums, all or most of the time had to be devoted to the technical areas. Within the past decade, general education has aroused increasing interest as educators and the lay public have felt the need for improvement in the social, civic, moral, and spiritual areas, and there has been a trend toward increasing the general education offerings.

2. The point of view which the administration adopts

regarding student personnel services. If an institute adopts the concept that it is interested in educating the *whole* student, the amount of consideration and provision made for admissions, housing, health services, counseling, and placement will influence the objectives.

3. The decision which is made regarding the desirability of offering cooperative work. Many educators would agree that learning by doing is one of the important principles in the psychology of learning. In practice, however, this principle has not always been included in the educational techniques used. Cooperative work programs seem particularly well suited to technical institutes, and the final decision which is made to include, or not to include, cooperative work will influence their objectives.

## Steps in preparing objectives

There is probably no single way in which the objectives of technical institutes now in existence have been decided upon. In some instances, an individual, or small group of individuals has felt the need for technical training and a new institution has been organized. It has then been the task of the educator to translate these needs to educational terms. In other cases an existing institution has felt the need to reexamine its program to determine the extent to which the needs of the community for this type of education are being met. A practical illustration of this latter approach is provided by the experience of the Rochester Institute of Technology. A going concern with a plant, faculty, and student body, this institution decided to reformulate its general objectives following World War I.

In this instance the earliest steps were taken by the president and the board of trustees. A committee of outside consultants was engaged to study the institution. The broad outlines of policy were determined by the president and the board after considering the report of the consultants. A more complete formulation of objectives was then undertaken in 1929, when each member of the faculty was called upon to make a statement of the contributions which he believed he was making or should make, through the Institute, to the lives of the students and to outline his objectives.

To focus his thinking, each faculty member was asked to respond to the following questions:

1. What characteristics should mark Institute graduates?
2. What educational objectives do you think the Institute stands for?
3. What are your personal objectives in teaching Institute students?
4. What changes in educational objectives would you suggest?

The statements of faculty members were assembled departmentally and general department objectives were formulated from them. The several department heads and the president then used the departmental statements as a basis for crystallizing the general objectives of the institution. To complete the circuit, the objectives were referred to individual faculty members so that curriculums and instruction could be checked against them.[3]

[3] Charters, *op. cit.*, p. 9.

Periodically, this process has been repeated at the Rochester Institute of Technology, and minor revisions of the statement of general objectives have resulted over the years. The current objectives of the Institute include service to students in respect to occupational competence, social competence, and personal development, with more specific objectives under each of these points. Further objectives are the integration and continual reevaluation of the total program. In the 1954–1955 catalogue of the Rochester Institute of Technology the institute's objectives are condensed as follows:[4]

> The basic objective of the Rochester Institute of Technology is to prepare students for effective and satisfying participation in a democratic and technological society. The Institute attempts to attain this objective by providing each student with a well-rounded program which will assist him to (1) earn a living in a suitable occupational field; (2) acquire appropriate attitudes toward work; (3) develop the capacity for intelligent voting, effective parenthood, and assumption of other community responsibilities; (4) understand himself and improve his abilities to get along with other people, and (5) develop appreciations and interests that are personally rewarding.

Examples of the steps utilized in preparing objectives are not easy to find in the literature on technical institute education. It appears that the men who have directed the institutes have been doers, rather than educational philosophers. L. V. Johnson, Director of Southern Technical

[4] Catalogue, Day Program, Rochester Institute of Technology, 1954–1955, Rochester, N.Y., p. 7.

Institute, has, however, pointed out the background of thinking which has served as a basis for formulating objectives for technical institutes operating as divisions of land-grant colleges. He has stated that the institutes serve four definite needs:[5]

1. To meet industrial demands, technical institutes train high school graduates for an estimated 150,000 positions opening annually.
2. Technical institutes meet a social need. Provision is made for the thousands of students who do not seek engineering degrees or who are handicapped by lack of mathematical ability.
3. There is an economic need, because existing college facilities are inadequate to handle the increasing college population, despite a growing desire for free education beyond the high school level. A two-year college system, including technical institutes, would often develop American youth more than a system composed entirely of four-year schools.
4. Technical institutes meet military needs. The national defense program is based upon technical superiority to potential enemies.

## Building a program

Once the general objectives of an institute have been formulated and it has been determined that there is need

[5] L. V. Johnson, "The Responsibility of Land-grant Colleges to Provide the Technical Institute Level of Education," *Proceedings of the Association of Land-grant Colleges and Universities*, November, 1950, p. 185.

for one or more curriculums, the following additional steps are essential:

1. To study the job requirements in the occupational fields selected and allocate the required knowledges, skills, and understandings to courses of instruction.

2. To recruit and select an instructional staff having experience in the required technical areas.

3. To plan a balance between the technical courses and the general education courses offered.

4. To decide whether any of the unique functions of technical institutes will be achieved, such as providing cooperative work experience or offering evening courses for employed adults.

5. To study the student personnel services which will be offered in the way of housing, food service, counseling, and job-placement service.

6. To make provision for recruiting and selecting the student body and carrying on a sound program of public relations.

7. To provide an administrative organization and staff that will be responsible for policy making, finances and business management, instruction, student personnel services, and public relations.

The foregoing steps will be considered in detail in the chapters which follow.

CHAPTER 7

# Surveying the Demand

It has been emphasized in this volume that each technical institute curriculum seeks to prepare graduates for some occupational field or cluster of jobs. The type and the number of employment opportunities, either present or potential, determine the types of curriculums which are appropriate for a technical institute to offer and the numbers of students it should attempt to accommodate. This implies some type of survey or study to determine the demand on the part of industry for technical institute education.

An equally important aspect of the demand for technical education is the interest or potential interest of prospective students. It will serve no purpose to offer curriculums in which students cannot be induced to enroll.

It is the purpose of this chapter to outline some of the more important considerations in surveying the demand on the part of industry for technical institute graduates, as well as the key factors in surveying the demand on the part of prospective students for technical institute curriculums. In view of the limited scope of this book, however, reference should be made to other sources for a more detailed outline of survey procedures.

### The scope of technical occupations

A problem inherent in determining the demand for technical institute education lies in the fact that statistics refer to the past, while education serves the future. Some industries and occupations are expanding, while others are contracting. Most changes in the labor forces develop gradually, however. This tends to give current statistics validity for a reasonable length of time. As a long-range activity, education is concerned not with short-term variations in employment but with long-term trends. Some idea of the potential field for technical institute education is shown in Table 27.

Occupational Class 1, as defined by the United States Census, includes designers, draftsmen, engineers, and technicians. Most of the occupational objectives of technical institute programs fall within this group. However, technical institute graduates often find employment in Classes 3 and 6, doing supervisory work requiring a technical background. Education of the technical institute type is likewise suitable preparation for a number of the clerical and sales jobs in Classes 4 and 5.

The occupational objectives of technical institute courses cut across the various census classifications in such a way that it is not possible to obtain from this source a precise estimate of the number of jobs for which technical institute preparation is appropriate. Nevertheless, the census figures make clear that there is a very substantial

TABLE 27

DISTRIBUTION OF THE LABOR FORCE IN 1950 BY OCCUPATIONAL CLASS

| Occupational Class | Number Employed | Per Cent of Total Labor Force |
|---|---|---|
| 1. Professional, technical, and kindred | 4,909,241 | 9 |
| 2. Farmers and farm managers | 4,306,253 | 8 |
| 3. Managers, officials, and proprietors | 5,017,465 | 9 |
| 4. Clerical and kindred | 6,894,374 | 12.5 |
| 5. Sales workers | 3,926,510 | 7 |
| 6. Craftsmen, foremen, and kindred | 7,772,560 | 14 |
| 7. Operatives and kindred | 11,146,220 | 20 |
| 8. Private household workers | 1,407,466 | 2.5 |
| 9. Service workers, except private household | 4,287,703 | 8 |
| 10. Farm laborers and foremen | 2,399,794 | 4 |
| 11. Laborers, except farm and mine | 3,417,232 | 6 |
| Total | 55,384,818 | 100.0 |

SOURCE: *Statistical Abstract of the United States*, Bureau of the Census, Washington, 1953.

number of such jobs and that they comprise a large percentage of the labor force.

In determining the realistic demand for graduates of an existing or proposed institution, it is necessary to define the area of service, in terms of both geography and occupation. Four principal approaches have been used, either singly or in combination:

1. Public education authorities have undertaken to serve all appropriate occupations which exist in sufficient numbers within an entire state. Statewide surveys of the need for technical institute education has been completed in New York State and in Louisiana.[1,2]

2. An institution has attempted to provide services for all appropriate occupations in its own geographical area, as in the case of Weber College in Ogden, Utah.

3. An institution has undertaken to serve a particular industry, as exemplified by RCA Institutes.

4. On a national basis an institution has set out to serve a particular occupation or field of work. This approach is used by the Rochester Institute of Technology in its curriculums in photography and printing.

## Preliminary steps in making a survey

The purpose of an occupational survey is to answer the question, "For what technical occupations should curriculums be provided?" In this connection it is important to clarify what is meant by technical occupation. In setting out to make a statewide survey, the New York State committee started with a definition of terms.[3]

> A technical occupation is a vocation requiring skillful application of a high degree of specialized knowledge together

[1] J. Cayce Morrison, chairman, *A Guide to the Development of Programs for the Institutes of Applied Arts and Sciences,* University of the State of New York, Albany, 1946.

[2] Thomas E. Hampton, *A Survey of Technical Occupations in Louisiana Industry,* State of Louisiana, Baton Rouge.

[3] Morrison, *op. cit.,* p. 27 (for further criteria identifying technical jobs, see p. 43).

with a broad understanding of operational procedures; involving the frequent application of personal judgement; usually dealing with a variety of situations; and often requiring supervision of the work of others. It offers the opportunity for the worker to develop an ever-increasing personal control over the application of his knowledge to his work and usually requires fewer motor skills than a trade or skilled occupation and less generalized knowledge than a profession.

This definition led to the following check list of criteria for identifying technical jobs:

1. Emphasizes technical knowledge.
2. Emphasizes technical skill (the ability to use technical knowledge).
3. Deals with rational processes as contrasted with empirical rules.
4. Has concern with cause and effect.
5. Emphasizes analysis and diagnosis.
6. Requires frequent exercise of ability to use involved judgment.
7. Deals with many factors and a large number of variables.
8. Contends with a large variety of situations.
9. Requires a knowledge of skilled work but not necessarily skill in doing it.
10. Requires a broad background of fundamental science and mathematics.
11. Involves use of a variety of instruments.
12. Requires effective use of language to interpret orders and make reports.

13. Involves the element of leadership in supervisory occupations.

14. Requires understanding of industrial equipment and processes.

15. Frequently involves visualization of plans and drawings, and a degree of creative design.

On the basis of the foregoing criteria occupations suitable for education of the technical institute type may be classified as follows:[4]

1. Engineering aides and science aides, such as drafting specialists and laboratory technicians, requiring a year or two of employment training.

2. The technical specialists or limited technicians, such as certain specialized instrument repairmen and certain types of inspectors, who can be trained in relatively short preemployment or preproduction courses.

3. The technical production and maintenance supervisors, who must have a background of industrial or trade experience, plus supplementary technical and foremanship training.

4. The semitechnical men, such as salesmen, whose basic training is in the field of distributive education, but who must have some technical knowledge of the things they sell, and factory accountants, whose basic training may be in the field of accounting, but who must have some technical knowledge of the plant and its products in order to understand and evaluate the figures they use.

[4] *Vocational-Technical Training for Industrial Occupations,* U.S. Office of Education Bulletin 228, Washington, 1944, pp. 22–23.

## Survey methods and procedures

The first step in connection with an occupational survey is to determine the main purpose to be served, or the information that is desired. It is probable that a single-curriculum survey of one occupation will achieve more meaningful results than a community-wide gathering of statistics. A single-curriculum survey is likely to yield more specified information with more direct applicability to the curriculum. On the other hand, it is clear that very useful results have been obtained by the broader surveys in Ogden, Utah, in New York State, in Louisiana, and in other areas.

The broad outlines of an occupational survey are likely to be determined by a group or committee. There is general agreement, however, that it is most efficient to put one person in charge of gathering and organizing data.

The most fundamental decision in respect to method is the source or sources of information. In most occupational surveys information is obtained from employers.[5] It is possible, however, to obtain information from workers. The purpose, scope, and content of the survey will determine the most appropriate source of information. If employers are to be surveyed, it is necessary to determine whether all or a sampling of employers in a given category will be used. In the Louisiana survey, for example, it was decided to include only those having more

[5] Marguerite Zapoleon, *Community Occupational Surveys,* U.S. Office of Education Bulletin 223, Washington, 1942, p. 27.

than 5000 employees.[6] The problem of sampling is equally important in making contacts with workers.

The second major decision regarding methods involves the techniques utilized to obtain information. One common technique is a questionnaire mailed to an employer. The questionnaire method is relatively inexpensive, but it has limited accuracy and usually produces no more than a 50 per cent return.[7] Advance publicity, careful wording, and brevity tend to increase questionnaire returns.

In the development of a questionnaire, it is particularly important to determine precisely the information that is desired and to formulate questions which will be clearly understood by those who are asked to complete it. This may require the combined efforts of several people, whose knowledge will include an understanding of educational objectives, of technical institute courses, and of the language of industry. In the past it has often been found in the tabulation of a questionnaire that some item was misinterpreted or that the device in some other way failed to achieve its purpose. There is more chance of avoiding this failure if the questionnaire is pretested on a small portion of the total survey population to determine its effectiveness before the main portion of the survey is completed.

Personal interviews are the chief alternative to questionnaires. Under this method, replies may be more comprehensive, provided that interviewers are carefully se-

[6] Hampton, *op. cit.*, p. 3.

[7] *Vocational-Technical Training for Industrial Occupations, op. cit.*, p. 261.

lected and trained. Interviews may be used to supplement questionnaires in cases where the returns are insufficient or not representative.

The use of interview methods brings up the problem of selecting and training interviewers. It is important to have interviewers who are thoroughly familiar with the industry or job cluster which they are surveying. A general question about the number of technicians employed would be unlikely to develop a comprehensive picture of the demand. Obtaining the needed information is likely to require that an interviewer ask about specific duties, skills, and training requirements of the jobs which may fall within the curricular area. Considerable interpretation may be needed to get the person interviewed to understand exactly the type of information sought. In this connection it may often be helpful to refer to a standard source of job descriptions, such as the *Dictionary of Occupational Titles*.[8]

An interviewer with appropriate experience and training will have an important advantage in knowing where to look for employment outlets in his field. Mechanical draftsmen, for example, might be employed in a wide variety of organizations. A pharmaceutical plant might employ printers, while a foundry might employ a chemical laboratory technician. A well-trained interviewer will have a realistic understanding of the placement market for technical institute graduates. He will be able to differentiate the work of the technician from that of the engi-

[8] *Dictionary of Occupational Titles,* U.S. Department of Labor, Washington, 1949.

neer, on the one hand, and the skilled craftsmen, on the other hand.

In planning interviews it is important to determine not only which plant or shop to visit but also what person to interview. Industrial contacts should be planned to reach persons who really know the jobs and processes under consideration.[9] One aspect of this problem is that an interviewer may obtain different answers from different individuals in the same plant. The broad knowledge and the specialized information available in a personnel office may be important to obtain in a survey, but somewhat different impressions may be obtained from a foreman having intimate knowledge of the individuals and jobs under his supervision. An interviewer with sound experience will know when to verify or expand the information obtained.

In an industrial survey it is important not only to obtain accurate data about jobs, but also to have an estimate of the number of job openings that will be available for technical institute graduates within a given period of time. Such an estimate requires knowledge of the total number of jobs, the annual replacement needs (this may vary according to the age of the incumbents), possible expansion of the number of jobs, trends in the industry's market, and other economic factors. It is often difficult to induce an employer to state his needs in simple quantitative terms, either because he is uncertain of them or be-

[9] *Vocational-Technical Training for Industrial Occupations, op. cit.*, p. 134.

cause he is unwilling to make any statement regarding a matter which involves factors beyond his control.

Detailed information on survey techniques may be found in Marguerite Zapoleon's bulletin on the subject.[10] An extensive bibliography on occupational surveys is presented by Phebe Ward.[11] One of the main purposes of presenting in this volume the amount of detail on surveys is to make clear the considerable amount of effort and time required. A poor survey may be worse than none in serving the purposes of a technical institute, and it is probable that a survey should not be undertaken unless there is adequate professional time available. To summarize, some of the basic questions which must be answered in planning and making a survey are:

1. Will the director be an institutional staff member or an outsider employed specifically for this purpose?

2. What staff members will work on the survey?

3. What office space, supplies, and equipment will be needed?

4. How much time will be required (based on the estimate of a person with appropriate knowledge and experience)?

5. Will all employers of a certain type be canvassed or will a sampling technique be employed?

6. How will the questionnaire or interview schedule be formulated?

[10] Zapoleon, *op. cit.*

[11] Phebe Ward, *Terminal Education in the Junior College*, Harper & Brothers, New York, 1947, pp. 153–55.

7. How will its applicability be pretested before the bulk of the survey is undertaken?

8. What experience of other institutions can be drawn upon to guide the survey planning?

**Determining the needs for technical curriculums**

Determining the numbers of persons employed in various technical occupations does not in itself show whether or not there is a need for technical institute education. In any occupation there may be an expanding or contracting demand for labor. Generally, however, it is estimated that annual replacement of employees amounts to about 5 per cent of the total employed.[12] Since educational institutions must plan on a long-range basis, this 5 per cent figure is used to determine how many graduates of a curriculum will be needed.

Another factor to be considered is the expected drop-out rate in a curriculum. One study showed that 60 per cent of the enrollees completed three-year cooperative programs in a technical institute.[13] The percentage might be higher for one-year or two-year programs. In proportion to the drop-out rate, more students would need to be enrolled than would be required in the occupation.

Other sources of education and training must also be considered. In the field for which a technical institute prepares graduates, many workers receive their training on the job. Others may have completed all or part of an

[12] Kenneth Beach et al., *Technical Occupations in the State of New York,* State Education Department, Albany, 1946, pp. 4–6.

[13] Leo F. Smith, "Student Survival in a Technical Institute," *Sch. Rev.,* vol. 53, p. 298, May, 1945.

engineering program. Morrison estimates that 75 per cent of the annual replacements in technician jobs would be filled by technical institute graduates if an adequate system of this type of education were available.[14]

## Surveying the interest of youth

Regardless of the demand on the part of industry, a technical institute curriculum will meet this demand only to the extent that it is able to enroll and graduate students. It is therefore important to gauge the interest of potential students in the curriculum.

As in the case of industry, this can be done by means of questionnaires and interviews. Since the students to be surveyed are usually in high school, any approach to them would usually require full cooperation on the part of the schools in the area.

The results of any simple questionnaire asking students about their educational plans or hopes should be examined with great caution. In such questionnaires it has usually been found that many students will unrealistically list an inordinate number of prestige occupations like physician, lawyer, engineer, and accountant. Another problem in this connection is that many high school students have little knowledge of the technical institute fields of instruction. Considerable interpretation may be needed before any meaningful response can be obtained. Interviews may be more useful than questionnaires in this respect, but the number of students who would be involved presents a serious limitation.

[14] Morrison, *op. cit.*, p. 31.

Effective high school guidance counselors are likely to be able to make a more accurate appraisal of their students' educational intentions than an outside interviewer, but the results of counselor surveys should likewise be viewed with caution. In deciding whether to initiate a new curriculum, one technical institute called a meeting of eighteen guidance counselors of the area. In going around the table, the counselors reported a total of thirty of their seniors whom they were quite sure would enroll in the new program. Acting on this information, the institute initiated and publicized the program, which actually enrolled only six students the first year and eight the second year.

In some areas of technical institute education one of the most important sources of students is the industry served. In such fields it would be desirable to survey the industry for potential students, but the same cautions should be observed in interpreting results.

If the need for a technical institute curriculum is to be determined, it is important to find out not only how many potential students are interested *now,* but also how many *can be* interested in the program. The motivation for occupational advancement is likely to be strong on the part of technical institute students. It may be possible to interest substantial numbers in a curriculum they may have not previously thought about if it can be shown that industry offers attractive careers in this field. In short, the promotional activities have an important bearing on potential enrollment.

In view of the number of variables which are difficult to

measure, a technical institute will often find it expedient to utilize the principle of the pilot study. In any field where an appropriate demand on the part of industry has been established, it would be reasonable to offer a curriculum on a trial basis for several years. The number of students who actually enroll after suitable promotional work provides the only really adequate test of the interest of youth in the curriculum.

## Summary

The common objective of all technical institutes is to prepare graduates for competence in a technical occupation. This makes it imperative for technical institute educators to study the knowledge and skills required in the occupations selected. It is equally essential to determine the demand on the part of industry for graduates of a technical curriculum.

This chapter has outlined considerations, methods, and procedures in making surveys of the potential demand for technical institute graduates. The following questions might be used as a guide in planning and executing such surveys:

1. Will the survey procedures be scientifically planned and objectively utilized, without reference to vested interests and preconceived ideas?
2. What industries or geographical areas will the survey cover?
3. Who will plan and make the survey?
4. What training, preparation, and technical assistance will be provided for survey personnel?

5. What methods and procedures will be used?

6. Who will prepare the report and what general form will it take?

7. What facilities, personnel, and finances will be available for making use of survey findings?

8. What will be done to determine whether young people will be interested in enrolling in the proposed curriculums?

CHAPTER 8

# Developing Curriculums

Technical institutes first developed in response to the need for filling certain positions in industry. The requirements of these positions were analyzed informally, and an attempt was made to recruit teachers with appropriate skills and knowledge. The skills of the machinists and draftsmen comprised one type of element in technical institute curriculums. Another element was provided by teachers of mathematics and science, who represented a more academic tradition. The clearly defined vocational focus of each curriculum provided a common bond, but the development of curriculums most appropriate for their objectives has long been a matter of primary concern to technical institute educators.

The authors of the 1931 SPEE study invited technical institutes to submit problems that should be considered. The one mentioned most frequently was curriculum content.[1] The immediate goal of employability of graduates makes technical institute faculties particularly aware of

[1] William E. Wickenden and Robert H. Spahr, *A Study of Technical Institutes*, Society for the Promotion of Engineering Education, Lancaster, Pa., 1931, p. 124.

the relationship between curriculum and student achievements. In other types of institutions it has been possible to broaden curriculums to include practically anything that might possibly be useful to the graduate, but the short length of the technical institute courses limits them to the essentials. Over the years there has been a constant struggle between time limitations and the desirability of including additional curriculum content.

Technical institute students are recruited on the premise that the curriculum is the one best and quickest pathway to a particular occupational objective. This clear definition of purpose makes the curriculum relatively inflexible. At the same time, it places unusual responsibility upon the curriculum planner. This responsibility is increased by the fact that technical institute programs are intended to be terminal rather than preparatory. Incentive to evaluate and justify technical institute curriculums has also come from their untraditional place in the educational scene. This combination of factors has sparked an unusual amount of pioneering by technical institutes in curriculum construction.

## Approaches to curriculum construction

In education, as in other pursuits, there are more followers than pioneers. An unfortunately common approach to curriculum construction is the "scissors and paste-pot method," in which existing curriculums in the same field are examined and adopted, in whole or in part.

A slightly more penetrating approach is to obtain the

opinion of experts about curriculum content. Technical institutes using this method have drawn upon both industrial experts and educators for curriculum ideas.

A third approach to curriculum building might be called the deductive method. This involves starting with the institute's objectives and from them determining the changes in students' knowledge, skills, and attitudes which the curriculum will attempt to bring about. The course content is then deduced by a logical reasoning process.

A fourth method of curriculum construction, which emphasizes activity analysis, might be called the inductive method. Starting with objectives, this method identifies the occupational and nonoccupational activities for which students are to be prepared. Then these activities are studied by firsthand observation, by examining job descriptions, diaries, and the like, and by obtaining information from experts. On the basis of the activities analyzed, an inductive reasoning process is used to determine the knowledge, skills, and other factors which should be included in the curriculum in order to achieve the objectives.

There is no one method of curriculum construction which is best for every situation, and in practice technical institutes often have made effective use of a combination of methods. Perhaps because of their common occupational focus, technical institutes have pioneered in the inductive method, particularly in respect to techniques of job analysis. In this connection it is important to bear in mind that before a job is analyzed for curriculum items, the institute's objectives must be determined and there should be some type of survey to determine the potential demand for graduates, as discussed in the preceding chapters.

## Studying job requirements

In building a curriculum inductively from activity analysis, a basic step is to ascertain the requirements for initial employment and advancement. These requirements are clarified by the construction of a job-cluster chart (illustrated in Chapter 5), which shows the basic, supplementary, and related jobs in a particular field of endeavor, or job cluster. The job chart is an aid in visualizing the training and intermediate jobs an employee passes through before he reaches his ultimate vocational goal. It also takes into consideration the fact that somewhere along this pathway a person may be diverted to a related job requiring similar skills and knowledge.

The New York State committee determined the appropriateness of each job-cluster chart as a basis for a technical institute curriculum by means of the following criteria:[2]

1. The curriculum is designed to prepare persons for a cluster of jobs in a given field, rather than for one specific payroll job.
2. The jobs included in the cluster meet the following conditions:

[2] J. Cayce Morrison, chairman, *A Guide to the Development of Programs for the Institutes of Applied Arts and Sciences.* The University of the State of New York, Albany, 1946, p. 19.

*a.* There are a sufficient number of different jobs in the cluster to provide a reasonable spread of job opportunities for the person graduated from the curriculum.
*b.* Each job in the cluster is of technician character (see check list, Appendix 4).
*c.* The jobs are of the level that normally require post–high school maturity with one to two years of training.
*d.* The jobs are closely associated with each other in industry so that shifting of the worker from one job to another in the cluster is readily possible and one job leads naturally to other more advanced jobs.
*e.* Important elements are found which are common to all the jobs, or in the preparation needed for them, such as common basic science and mathematics, common industrial terminology, and similar technical skills.

3. The curriculum content meets the following conditions:
   *a.* The range of the content needed in preparation for the jobs in the cluster is reasonable.
   *b.* The technical content lends itself to organized school instruction.
   *c.* A substantial portion of the total curriculum content consists of technical courses peculiar to the job cluster or basic thereto.
   *d.* The difficulty level of the content is such that it can be mastered by a reasonably high proportion of all high school graduates.
   *e.* Most students pursuing the curriculum can complete the required work in two years or less of full-time study.
4. The curriculum title describes it so clearly that it is easily identified and understood by employers and prospective students.
5. The placement opportunities (in industry) in the entry or

training jobs in the cluster are sufficiently large to justify a special curriculum for this field.

6. It will be feasible to secure, maintain, and keep up to date the special equipment needed for this curriculum.
7. Adequate and satisfactory facilities for training in this field are not now available.

## Activity analysis and curriculum content

Although the job chart is a valuable aid in visualizing the scope of a curriculum, it does not in itself indicate the content of the courses. It is necessary to analyze the jobs in the chart from the standpoint of duties and responsibilities, in order to determine the essential knowledge, skills, and attitudes, especially for the basic job. In making these analyses, it has been found desirable to record both the activities which are carried on during the day's program and traits or qualities of personality which a person must possess in order to carry on the activities efficiently.[3] This means that the techniques of industrial job analysis must be supplemented by other approaches.

Emerson suggests that appropriate information might be classified into the following categories:[4]

Basic technical information
Specialized technical information
Basic technical skills (ability to apply technical information to practical jobs)

[3] Mark Ellingson, "Activity Analysis as a Basis for Course Content," *Personnel J.*, vol. 12, p. 13, June, 1933.

[4] *Vocational-Technical Training for Industrial Occupations*, U.S. Office of Education Bulletin 228, Washington, 1944, pp. 267–268.

Technical judgment
Supervisory skills and knowledge
Manipulative skills
Industrial organization practices
Human relationships

In a series of occupational studies at the Rochester Institute of Technology, consultants were employed to assist in planning. Department heads and members of the faculty performed various phases of the analyses. The methods used in these studies are shown in Table 28.

The various lists referred to at several points in Table 28 are records of the activities carried on in performing a job. At the first stage, they may be listed in random order. In a second stage of analysis the activities are grouped according to functions. Then they are numbered consecutively and arranged in a form comparable to that of a logical outline. In short, an activity analysis is a logically organized list of activities performed on a job. An excerpt from an activity analysis of a tool engineer's typical duties follows (numbers are those used for indexing in the complete activity analysis):[5]

71. He makes electrical power calculations.
    72. He designs jigs, fixtures, special gauges, and machine parts involving electrical circuits, stops, relays, gauging elements, magnetic and electronic devices.
    73. He lays out electrical circuit diagrams.
74. He makes use of simple theory of lenses, mirrors, and prisms

[5] Sherman Hagberg, "Engineering a Tool Engineering Curriculum," *Tool Engr.*, May, 1945, pp. 28–32.

TABLE 28

METHODS USED IN MAKING ACTIVITY ANALYSES AS A BASIS FOR CURRICULUMS IN NINE DEPARTMENTS OF THE ROCHESTER INSTITUTE OF TECHNOLOGY

| Method | Retailing | Food Administration | Construction Supervision | Chemistry | Art | Electrical | Mechanical | Foremanship | Photographic Technology |
|---|---|---|---|---|---|---|---|---|---|
| Initial list by investigator | x | x | x | x | x | x | x | x | x |
| Diary lists |  | x |  |  |  | x |  |  |  |
| Interviews | x | x | x | x | x | x | x | x | x |
| Lists by graduates |  | x |  | x | x | x |  |  |  |
| Working on the job | x | x | x | x | x | x |  | x | x |
| Observing | x | x |  | x |  | x | x | x |  |
| Analyses found in literature | x | x |  |  |  |  |  |  | x |
| General technical literature | x | x | x | x | x | x | x | x | x |
| Analyzing type jobs |  |  | x | x | x | x |  |  |  |
| Check by Rochester experts | x | x | x | x | x | x | x | x | x |
| Check by others | x | x | x | x | x | x |  | x |  |
| Conference of checkers |  | x |  | x |  |  |  |  |  |
| Conference of Institute investigators | x | x | x | x | x | x | x | x | x |

SOURCE: Mark Ellingson, "Activity Analysis as a Basis for Course Content," *Personnel J.*, vol. 12, p. 13, June, 1933.

in the design of certain gauging devices and assembly fixtures.

75. He applies principles of hydraulics to design of hydraulically operated machines and fixtures.
    76. He applies principles of hydraulics to design of rubber forming dies.
77. He applies principles of hydraulics to plastic flow of metals in:
    78. Punch press work.
    79. Extrusion of metals through extrusion dies.
80. He solves algebraic, geometric, and trigonometric problems in:
    81. Design of tools, dies, and fixtures.
    82. Electrical power calculations.
    83. Strength-of-materials calculations.
    84. Force, velocity and time calculations.
85. He solves problems involving occasional use of calculus in
    87. Centers of gravity.
    88. Moments of inertia.

The logical ordering and numbering of items in an activity analysis facilitates regrouping and manipulation of items in the process of curriculum construction. The analysis must be carried to sufficient detail tó give an instructor a clear picture of the contribution that his course makes to performance on the job.

It should be emphasized that a list of activities or responsibilities of a job cannot be viewed as permanent and static. Additions or changes may be necessary as new developments in the field are brought to light through reports of graduates or other sources. It should be noted, however, that activity analyses made by the Rochester

Institute of Technology in twenty-two occupational areas after a five-year interval showed no major changes.[6]

## Planning courses of instruction

In curriculum construction based upon analyses of activities and responsibilities, the next step is to allocate each duty to some course of instruction. A simple but practical technique that has been used for this purpose is to make a list of the courses which seem to represent the major areas of content. It is then possible to use each of these course titles as a heading under which may be placed the numbers of the activities which most appropriately fit into that course. Subsequent steps in this type of curriculum construction are

1. Obtain faculty agreement on allocation of duties to courses.
2. Organize instructional materials into units.
3. Arrange units according to logical and psychological considerations.
4. Set up schedules and appropriate allocations of credit.

As compared with other approaches to curriculum construction, it is claimed that the foregoing method has the following advantages:[7]

1. Facilitates the elimination of duplication and superfluous materials.

[6] Mark Ellingson, *Determining the Professional Courses in a Technical Institute's Curricula,* unpublished doctoral dissertation, Ohio State University, 1936, p. 129.

[7] Ellingson, *op. cit.,* p. 15.

2. Tends to provide greater incentive by virtue of its showing relationship between activities and content.

3. Assists in providing stabilized and validated courses even though instructors may change.

4. Aids in providing content prepared for a specific vocational objective in contrast to general content.

Most occupational curriculums in technical institutes are derived from procedures resembling those described in the foregoing, although in many instances the techniques are less elaborate or some steps are omitted. Some technical institute curriculums, especially those in proprietary institutions, are limited exclusively to occupational elements. However, as indicated in Tables 16 and 17, they may include courses in the technical specialty, allied technical specialties, basic science, and administrative and managerial functions.

## The place of general education

Although the central goal of technical institutes continues to be the development of occupational competence, there is a growing feeling that occupational preparation alone is not enough. This has brought about a trend toward increasing the offerings in general education, which has been defined as "that part of a student's education which looks first of all to his life as a responsible human being and citizen."[8]

Educators are in agreement that there is need for all

[8] Harvard University Committee on General Education, *General Education in a Free Society,* Harvard University Press, Cambridge, 1946, p. 51.

students taking courses in general education—a point which engineering educators have emphasized since World War II—but there is no common agreement as to what the content of these courses should be. Numerous articles have been written on the subject, a professional magazine is published in this field, and foundations have given substantial grants of money to enable colleges and universities to develop curriculums in general education, but still the quest continues. In the light of all this discussion, the authors of this book have no illusions that what is written in the brief paragraphs which follow will solve the problem of determining the optimum general education content for a technical institute. It is hoped, however, that these paragraphs will identify some of the factors which should be kept in mind in formulating a general education program.

The objectives of general education are listed in detail in an American Council on Education pamphlet.[9] For the purposes of this book, however, it may be sufficient to utilize Davis'[10] list of the six areas of education with which a technical institute (or any other institution) should concern itself:

1. Occupational competence.
2. Citizenship effectiveness.
3. A reasonable understanding of nature and her laws.
4. Recreational and aesthetic activities.

[9] Dorothy L. McGrath, ed., *A Design for General Education.* American Council on Education, Washington, 1944, pp. 30–50.

[10] Warren Davis, "Vocational and Liberal Education—Unity or Duality," *Sch. Soc.*, vol. 55, p. 272, March 7, 1942.

5. Participation in general social activities.
6. Proper use of leisure time.

It is evident that courses in drafting, machine shop, and direct-current circuits will do relatively little toward meeting these nonoccupational objectives. Instead, courses in the social sciences, humanities, and the arts are suggested.

The New York State committee on technical institute curriculums proposed the following principles as a guide in developing general education courses:[11]

1. Science and mathematics should be utilized as a broad base for technical specialization as well as a means of personal and social orientation.
2. A level of oral and written expression should be developed which is appropriate to the student's vocational, personal, and social needs.
3. An improved understanding of personal, social, and civic problems should be developed to assist the student in discharging his responsibilities as an individual, a citizen, a worker, and a home administrator.
4. Reading and the other communication arts should be utilized for their potential contribution to personal, social, and occupational life.
5. Emphasis should be placed on the improvement and maintenance of the student's personal health and the sharing of responsibility for community health.

The special nature of the technical institute makes it important to study not only the content of general education courses but also their organization within the cur-

[11] Morrison, *op. cit.*, pp. 48–49.

riculum. Since technical institute programs are both short and terminal, there is insufficient time to develop a series of general education courses proceeding from a survey at an elementary level to advanced study in more specialized areas, as is possible in a liberal arts college. Almstead states that instead of this vertical curriculum building, "general studies for a two-year program should be built horizontally—should draw knowledge from across the board so that the student receives a unit of integrated knowledge about an event."[12]

## Planning general education content

In analyzing a job it is not difficult to find general agreement among all persons familiar with the job regarding the essential elements which should be included in a curriculum designed to prepare students for that job. In the field of general education, however, there is much more room for legitimate disagreement and experts often differ widely. The opinion of experts may have a more important place in determining general education content than in building technical courses, and the underlying philosophy of the administrators is likely to determine which experts are consulted.

The inductive method, utilizing activity analysis, may be followed in developing general education courses as well as technical courses. This method was used for an unpublished study by Warren Davis at the Rochester Institute of Technology in some of its earlier work in de-

[12] Francis E. Almstead, "A Design for General Education in Technical Institutes," *Tech. Educ. News,* Special Issue, 1954.

veloping the general education content of its curriculums. In a manner somewhat comparable to the job analysis technique, the General Education faculty compiled a list of twenty-one major areas of human activity of concern to the college age group in our society. These were education; thinking; mental hygiene; physical hygiene; foods; clothing; shelter; communication; transportation; friendship; pre-marriage and family relations; civic and political relations; other social relationships; recreation, reading; religion and/or philosophy; fine art (general); fine art (literature); fine art (drama); fine art (music); nature; personal finance.

This list of major activities and the subactivity areas included under them was checked and rechecked by faculty and students and by a sizable number of people living in the community. It was realized, however, that not all of these areas could be covered thoroughly in courses of two and three years duration. The elements considered most essential were selected in proportions designed to balance the technical elements of the curriculum in a ratio of approximately one to three. This need for selection and condensation in planning general education content of technical institute curriculums emphasizes the importance of subjective judgment and underlying philosophy. These are key factors even where systematic procedures such as activity analysis are utilized.

In spite of the philosophical and other factors which differentiate technical institutes, their common purposes and characteristics have led to some identifiable common patterns in general education offerings. Most institutes with significant amounts of general education include courses in English communication and in the social sciences. Languages are not taught, and it is usually felt that general education in the natural sciences is adequate as a result of the courses in physics, chemistry, and similar subjects which form an important element in the technical side of the curriculum. A survey covering 249 curriculums in 1954 showed the following frequencies for the general education subjects listed in Table 29.

TABLE 29

FREQUENCY OF GENERAL EDUCATION SUBJECTS

| Subject | Frequency |
|---|---|
| Report writing, technical writing, and communication skills | 169 |
| Psychology and human relations | 106 |
| Social science survey and government | 86 |
| English grammar and composition | 67 |
| Public speaking | 57 |
| Economics | 55 |

SOURCE: Edward E. Booher, "The Place of General Education in Technical Institute Curriculums," *Tech. Educ. News*, Special Issue, 1954.

## Typical technical institute curriculums

The preceding paragraphs in this chapter have been devoted to pointing out the importance of curriculum content, the various approaches to curriculum construction, the techniques of analyzing job requirements, the methods of using these analyses as the basis for curriculum planning, and the place of general education courses in the curriculum. Perhaps the easiest way to visualize what is actually offered is for the reader to study curriculums in electronics, radio, and television as offered by a publicly supported institute, a privately endowed institute, and a proprietary institute. These and other representative curriculums are shown in Appendix 5.

## General principles

In light of the research work which has been done in this field and the history of the most successful technical institutes, certain fundamental principles underlying technical institute curriculums may be listed:

1. The objectives of the curriculum should be clearly defined.
2. Curriculums should be offered only in occupational fields in which a potential demand for graduates has been definitely established.
3. Each curriculum should be designed to prepare a student for a related cluster of vocational-technical occupations. Occupational competence is an essential objective of each curriculum.
4. The curriculums should be related to the needs of industry.
5. An analysis should be made of the skills, attitudes, and knowledge essential for successful employment in the job cluster.
6. The occupational objectives for which the curriculums are designed should be attractive to students.
7. The curriculums should take into account the level and capacity of the students who will enroll.
8. The curriculums should be so organized that they

prepare a student for immediate productive employment upon graduation.

9. The institution should have or be able to obtain adequate plant, faculty, and facilities to achieve the objectives of the curriculums.

10. Attention should be paid to the relative values of different portions of the curriculum when determining time distribution.

11. The type and amount of general education in each curriculum should be determined with care, in light of the objectives of the institution.

12. Provision should be made for continual evaluation of each curriculum.

CHAPTER 9

# The Instructional Staff

The clear objective of developing occupational competence, which is shared by all technical institutes, is a key factor in determining the type of instructor who will be sought. The achievement of this objective requires instructors with experience in the technical subject matter which they teach. For instructors in general education subjects, "the first requisite is that general education and occupational education . . . be thought of as complementary parts of a larger whole."[1] In addition to these basic qualifications, the special nature of technical institutes creates a need for instructors "who do not shy away from the language and ways of everyday business—who can find satisfaction in careers in which they will be expected to identify themselves actively with working communities, as well as qualify for membership in a professional community."[2]

[1] *Wanted: 30,000 Instructors,* American Council on Education, Washington, 1949, p. 38.

[2] *Ibid.,* p. 3.

## Qualifications

The SPEE study in 1931 found that only 4 per cent of technical institute faculty members lacked industrial experience.[3] In a more recent study, Holderman surveyed 533 full-time instructors at eighteen institutes whose curriculums were accredited by ECPD. The average industrial experience of these instructors was five and a half years.[4] At one institution instructors averaged nine and a half years, and at the other end of the scale the institutional average for industrial experience was approximately one year.

In a questionnaire survey made by the authors in 1954, forty institutes responded. Usable replies were obtained from thirty-three institutes in answer to a question regarding their requirements for work experience on the part of their instructors. The requirements were as follows:

| Years experience required | Number of institutes |
|---|---|
| 8 | 1 |
| 7 | 1 |
| 6 | 0 |
| 5 | 5 |
| 4 | 0 |
| 3 | 6 |
| 2 | 2 |
| 1 | 1 |

[3] William E. Wickenden and Robert H. Spahr, *A Study of Technical Institutes,* Society for the Promotion of Engineering Education, Lancaster, Pa., 1931, p. 151.

[4] K. L. Holderman, "Some Facts About Our Technical Institute Instructors," *Tech. Educ. News,* April, 1952, p. 2.

One institute reported a requirement of five to ten years, another reported three to five years, and a third required two to five years. A number of institutes responded with more general statements, like those below:

"Few years."
"Industrial experience."
"Successful business and industrial experience."
"Thorough competence."
"Desired but not essential."
"Cases judged individually."
"Satisfactory experience."
"Desirable but not required due to shortage of engineers."

The Wickenden-Spahr report in 1931 stated, "It is evident that formal academic qualifications are not the primary criterion in selecting teachers."[5] Nevertheless, in many instances the competence required in a technical institute instructor depends in part upon the completion of a certain educational program. This is particularly true in the academic fields, such as mathematics, physics, and general education. At the time of the 1931 study, 70 per cent of technical institute instructors held college degrees.

Holderman[6] found that

> Forty-four per cent of 533 full-time teachers employed in 18 institutes developed as teachers through their training at technical institutes and trade schools or by serving apprenticeships and gaining practical technical experience. They

[5] Wickenden and Spahr, *op. cit.*, p. 150.
[6] Holderman, *op. cit.*, p. 1.

are not college graduates. The other 56 per cent hold degrees.

He also discovered that the range in the number of instructors having degrees varied from 8 to 100 per cent with a median of 65 per cent for the 18 institutions studied.

Holderman's study revealed that the educational preparation of faculties at institutions with a curriculum in a single technological field differed significantly from the background of faculties at schools offering several different technical curriculums. At the eight institutes surveyed which offered only one curriculum, 39 per cent of the teachers had academic degrees. In the ten schools offering more than one program, 74 per cent of the instructors had at least the bachelor's degree.[7]

Educational requirements for institute instructors in 1954 were as follows:

| Requirement | Number of institutes |
| --- | --- |
| Bachelor's degree | 28 |
| Technical institute graduate | 3 |
| Master's degree | 1 |
| High school graduate | 1 |

Several institutes reported that their degree requirements are for academic personnel and that the educational requirements for teachers of the trades are lower or not specified.

Among the qualifications of technical institute instructors, the intangible personal qualities that make a good

[7] *Ibid.*, p. 2.

teacher are usually rated as more important than a specified degree or number of years of work experience. These qualities were expressed by one administrator as "knowledge of his subject, sympathetic understanding of the student difficulties, ability to clearly present the subject and its relation to industry."[8] Another stated, "knowledge of industry and sympathy with aims of individual students."[9]

Van Zeeland, in a paper presented at the June, 1951, meeting of the Technical Institute Division at Michigan State College, had the following to say:[10] "It is obvious that the technical institute instructor must possess many characteristics. These qualities can be classified into three groups—the predominantly psychological, those which are largely technical, and the physical and manual."

The American Council on Education in 1945 called a conference to study specifically the problem of the preparation of teachers for junior colleges and technical institutes. Following this conference a bulletin was published which concludes:[11] "In short, this is a job for thoughtful, stouthearted men and women, with certain traits—willing to step outside traditional academic circles in any important cause, not afraid of pioneer confusions and growing pains, or of temporary junior status, or of the direct speech of the factory, the farm, the store, the newspaper office, or the city hall."

[8] Wickenden and Spahr, *op. cit.*, p. 153.

[9] *Ibid.*, p. 154.

[10] Fred J. VanZeeland, "Desirable Characteristics of a Technical Institute Instructor," *Tech. Educ. News*, January, 1952, p. 2.

[11] ACE, *op. cit.*, p. 8.

## Sources of recruitment

Most technical institutes are on the alert for instructors who possess the desired qualities, and their recruitment is not limited to any single source. The forty institutes responding to the authors' survey in 1954 reported the sources of recruitment for instructors shown in Table 30.

TABLE 30

RECRUITMENT OF INSTRUCTORS

| Source of recruitment | Number of institutes utilizing source |
|---|---|
| Advertisements in newspapers and trade journals | 7 |
| College placement offices | 7 |
| Secondary school teachers and teacher agencies | 7 |
| Industry | 6 |
| Institute's own graduates | 6 |
| Personal contacts of faculty | 4 |
| State employment service | 3 |
| State bureau | 3 |
| Private employment agencies | 2 |
| Professional organizations | 2 |
| Unsolicited applications | 1 |
| Industrial teacher training service | 1 |
| Retired public school personnel | 1 |
| Retired Army and Navy men | 1 |
| Referrals by staff members and engineers in parent company (RCA) | 1 |

Several of the institutes listed more than one source of recruitment for instructors, and it is apparent that no institute limits itself to a single source. In connection with the foregoing list, it is interesting to note that five of the seven institutes utilizing college placement offices were state-supported, as were all three of the institutes utilizing state bureaus. Otherwise, there was no particular relationship between the source of support and source of recruitment. As indicated by the foregoing list, there is no one best source of recruitment.

## Preparation

For teaching in most types of institutions, an adequate preparation for a beginning job can be obtained in a single educational program designed for that purpose. The preparation of a technical institute instructor, however, is complicated by the need for industrial experience and for adjusting to an institution which frequently does not fit into traditional patterns. As Jarvie states,[12]

> . . . it would appear that the goal should be the production of instructors who possess the following: (1) a clear and realistic understanding of the philosophy and purposes of technical institutes; (2) knowledge and techniques for analyzing and putting such a philosophy into action; (3) a functional ability in dealing with the complex factors of human growth and development; (4) mastery of a field of knowledge in a broad and relevant sense; and (5) the ability to develop new curriculum patterns and to bring to the entire undertaking an objective, evaluative point of view.

[12] Lawrence L. Jarvie, "Preparation of Technical Institute Instructors is Challenge to Schools," *Tech. Educ. News,* March, 1948, p. 6.

The degree from an engineering college indicates a level of achievement which is an adequate technical foundation for most technical institute instructorships. In many instances graduation from the technical institute itself may be appropriate. However, a technical foundation is only one of the requirements. Experience in industry, which is required for most technical institute teaching positions, must be obtained apart from educational preparation. Neither the industrial nor the educational side of an instructor's preparation is specifically designed to develop the necessary personal qualifications.

A typical example of the preparation of a technical institute instructor is provided by the case of an engineering graduate who wanted to become a technical institute faculty member. He felt that his background was geared too closely to the professional schools to be of much value to a technical institute. Consequently, for approximately two years he worked in industry, first, to gain experience in the practical application of engineering theory, and second, to study types of experience essential to persons filling technician jobs.[13]

Because of the problem of finding appropriately prepared technical institute faculty members, the California Junior College Federation in November, 1946, passed the following resolution:[14]

> . . . that the California Federation of Junior Colleges request the presidents of the teacher training institutions to

[13] ACE, *op. cit.*, p. 42.
[14] *Ibid.*, p. 40.

establish a program of teacher education that will train instructors in engineering and science in order to create a supply of appropriately trained instructors for the technical institute courses.

Only recently has there been an attempt to meet this long-felt need. The Oklahoma Institute of Technology now provides an opportunity for a student to combine a technical institute curriculum with preparation for teaching in a four-year program.[15] This is accomplished through cooperation between the technical institute division and the division which prepares trade and industrial teachers. Technical institute courses are given full credit in this baccalaureate degree program.

Another step to assist in the development of technical institute faculty taken during the summer of 1950 was the

[15] In an unpublished manuscript, H. P. Adams cites the following advantages of the Oklahoma plan:

1. The adoption of this program by several well-recognized industrial teacher training programs would result in providing an outlet for well-qualified technical institute graduates who wish to secure a four-year degree.
2. It definitely establishes that ECPD-approved technical institutes programs are of college level.
3. This program provides a most effective group of educational and vocational field counselors who are almost certain to be enthusiastic ambassadors of technical institute education.
4. It provides a proving ground for prospective teachers which should result in an increasing supply of more efficient teachers.
5. The plan will also provide a new source of exceptionally well-qualified, high-type teachers of industrial subjects. Many of the ECPD-approved technical institute curriculums offer more practical technical courses than those offered by the leading industrial teacher-training institutions.

holding of a workshop at Purdue University for technical institute teachers and administrators. Maurice Graney, who was at that time head of the Technical Institute Division at Purdue, outlined the twofold objectives of this workshop as follows:[16]

> The first objective was to bring together both administrators and teachers for an intensive study of the many issues now being resolved in the operation of technical institute programs. . . .
>
> The second objective was to make rather definite recommendation regarding the establishment of training programs for prospective technical-institute teachers.

Graney concluded that much was accomplished toward the first objective but that the second objective was less comprehensively achieved because it presupposed a concerted effort on the part of appropriate schools. Undoubtedly this workshop did serve as a stimulus to other schools to give consideration to similar programs.

## In-service training

As President Mark Ellingson, of the Rochester Institute of Technology, stated at a 1945 conference, most technical institute instructors have had to be made into teachers on the job.[17] Although most faculty members come to their jobs with reasonable mastery of their technology,

[16] Maurice R. Graney, "Purdue's Summer Workshop Draws Cross Section of Technical Institute Personnel," *Tech. Educ. News*, October, 1950, pp. 1–2.

[17] ACE, *op. cit.*, p. 40.

they are frequently lacking in knowledge and skill in educational principles and techniques. One solution to this problem lies in providing suitable training for instructors.

In the authors' 1954 survey, technical institutes were asked to indicate their in-service training programs for faculty members. The 40 responding institutes listed the following:

| In-service training program | Number of institutes reporting |
|---|---|
| On-campus training programs in pedagogy and related subjects | 11 |
| Faculty meetings, committees, and other informal training | 6 |
| Encourage or require off-campus training | 3 |
| On-campus training in technical subjects | 1 |

One of the on-campus training programs is a summer course by a specialist (New Hampshire Technical Institute). Two institutes enroll new instructors in regular classes covering fields in which they lack background. Two of the New York State institutes provide in-service training programs in cooperation with the New York State School of Labor and Industrial Relations.

The most common type of in-service training consists of discussions or seminars, although lectures may be used. Sessions typically cover instructional methods, technical institute history and philosophy, financing, and community relationships. Appendix 6 includes an outline of the in-service course at the New York City Community College of Applied Arts and Sciences.[18] Like any other aspect of an educational program, training sessions vary according to differences in institute objectives and curriculums.

Technical competence and skill in pedagogy are required in a technical institute instructor, but these factors will provide the optimum result only if the total atmosphere of the institute is appropriately stimulating. These intangible factors, which are so important to institute instructors, have been summarized by Jarvie as follows:[19]

> If teachers are to continue to grow in technical institutes, faculty members must be given an opportunity and encouragement to work on specific problems related to the improvement of their teaching. Provision must be made for the interchange of ideas and techniques between all faculty members, regardless of fields of specialization. Consultation services need to be provided, but these services must be such that consultants function as stimulators of thought on local problems. Consideration, encouragement, and opportunity must be given instructors to participate in all types of community activities and to become one with their community. Leaves of absence should be provided for instructors to obtain jobs outside the institution and away from the educational profession. Above all, the in-service program must be a program that evolves through group thinking of the faculty. Each faculty member must feel that the particular problems upon which he is working are significant to his becoming a more effective instructor.

[18] Personal communication from Dr. Otto Klitgord.
[19] Jarvie, *op. cit.*, p. 6.

## Instructional methods and materials

The technical institute aims to teach both the "how" and the "why" of an occupation. However, in order to develop occupational competence in a limited time, the theoretical aspects of subject matter tend to be emphasized less than in the engineering college. Instead, the application of principles is stressed. As Wickenden and Spahr[20] stated in 1931, "There is a manifest endeavor to teach underlying physical principles thoroughly, but not profoundly."

In the 1931 survey, technical institutes were asked to state the ways in which their teaching methods differed from those of engineering colleges. Some typical replies were:[21]

> . . . founded on engineering teaching, with limited list of subjects, taken many times each week, large percentage of drawing, laboratory, and shop work, and considerable outside study necessary. (Ohio Mechanics Institute)
>
> . . . less dependence on lectures. (Pratt)
>
> . . . greater use of project method. (Westinghouse)

Technical institutes have retained a much greater degree of individuality than have secondary schools and colleges. For this reason, many instructors have had no alternative but to prepare their own textbooks and manuals. In some instances filmstrips and moving pictures have also been specially prepared for technical institute instruction.

[20] Wickenden and Spahr, *op. cit.*, p. 157.
[21] *Ibid.*, pp. 159–160.

One of the greatest handicaps which technical institute administrators and instructors have had to face in the past has been the lack of adequate textbooks. In many cases the traditional college engineering textbooks were too abstract and presupposed a knowledge of calculus. On the other hand, books prepared for trade schools were inadequate because of the lack of attention paid to the understanding and appreciation of basic principles. The McGraw-Hill Book Company, Inc., long recognized this need and, in order to encourage instructors in technical-terminal programs to prepare texts, sponsored a contest from December, 1947, through August, 1949, and offered cash prizes for the best manuscripts submitted.[22] Numerous manuscripts were received and several were published. The winners of the contest were announced in March, 1950.[23]

### Teaching loads

In general, technical institute instructors are busy people. In his survey of eighteen accredited institutes, Holderman[24] found that the average teaching load of full-time faculty members was 23½ hours weekly. This includes only definitely scheduled time in classroom and laboratory. It does not include time spent in preparing for classes, in preparing and correcting tests, in counseling,

[22] "McGraw-Hill Announces Awards for Technical-Terminal Books," *Tech. Educ. News,* December, 1947, p. 3.

[23] "Ayres Places First in Junior College Textbook Contest," *Tech. Educ. News,* March, 1950, p. 4.

[24] Holderman, *op. cit.,* p. 5.

and in other contacts with students. At the institution with the heaviest teaching load, the faculty averaged 40 hours per week in class and laboratory. At the institute where the load was lightest, the faculty averaged 16½ hours. Between these extremes there was a distinct plateau from 19 to 24 hours. These figures may be compared with the 1931 report, which showed a teaching load ranging from 18 to 35 hours per week.[25]

Teaching loads at technical institutes are somewhat higher than are the loads at most colleges and universities. Technical institute class size, however, tends to be moderate or low, and the large lecture sections common at many higher institutions are almost never found.[26]

## Summary

The technical competence required of most technical institute instructors usually must be acquired through experience in industry. In addition to industrial experience,

[25] Wickenden and Spahr, *op. cit.*, p. 163.

[26] In a personal communication, Dr. Otto Klitgord has described the situation at the New York City Community College of Applied Arts and Sciences as follows: "The range and teaching load for our faculty are as follows: Our average class size is 25, with a maximum for special lectures of 35, and a minimum for special laboratory work of 12. The average teaching load for faculty is 18 hours per week; some teaching unprepared shop subjects carry as high as 24 hours, while others teaching difficult, prepared classes might teach as little as 15 hours. Department heads teach approximately six hours per week. Our ratio of faculty to student body is approximately 1 for 17. Insofar as possible, the faculty are programmed so that the number of preparations per day will not exceed three; the average is slightly over two."

most technical institute instructors hold college degrees. In the technical institute faculty member, however, personal qualities are more important than formal education or experience. For this reason, and because technical institutes do not fit into traditional educational patterns, recruitment of instructors utilizes a variety of sources, such as college and secondary school facilities, industry, and the institute's own graduates. Only one institution has begun a program of study specifically designed to prepare graduates for teaching positions in technical institutes.

To bridge the gap between varied preparation of faculty applicants and the needs of technical institute education, many institutes operate in-service training programs for faculty members. Technical institutes have also been forced to prepare a considerable proportion of their own textbooks and teaching materials. Teaching loads in technical institutes average higher than in colleges and universities, partly because of the higher percentage of shop and laboratory work.

CHAPTER 10

# Recruiting and Selecting Students

A technical institute—or any other educational institution—would not exist without a student body. Students are induced to enroll only to the extent that they are convinced that the institution will meet needs which are important to them.

At many liberal arts colleges, a student may enroll because of the social contacts, the beautiful campus, the renowned athletic teams, or the distinguished professors or because Uncle George went there. In contrast, the technical institute student places less emphasis on these factors than on the specific course of study leading to an occupational goal in which he is interested. This occupational field represents certain social and economic goals on the part of the student. In addition, the choice of a technical institute curriculum typically follows the student's specific interest in the activities which are common to both the institute and the job, such as drafting, mathematical calculations, or chemistry laboratory operations.

In order to determine the factors which influenced students to enroll, a questionnaire was administered for three successive years to freshmen at the Rochester Institute of

Technology.[1] Of these freshmen, 21 per cent checked the Institute's reputation in its technical field or its physical plant; 19 per cent came because of the "short, intensive courses." Financial considerations, contacts with R.I.T. faculty and staff, and influence of high school faculty members followed in that order as the most important factors bringing students to R.I.T.

It is important to note that the foregoing tabulation was noticeably influenced by relatively large enrollments in the departments of photography and printing, which attract students from all over the country. Financial considerations were the most important influence bringing students to the mechanical, electrical, and chemistry departments, which have cooperative programs and recruit from a more localized geographical area.

## How are students recruited?

To operate efficiently, any institution must maintain enrollment at a level commensurate with its facilities. In most cases this necessitates a continuing program of recruitment. The forty institutes which replied to the authors' survey question in 1954 reported use of the techniques of recruitment and related public relations activities shown in Table 31.

A study of the foregoing table reveals that the recruiting techniques used by technical institutes can be grouped into the following categories: personal contacts off the

[1] Laurence Lipsett and Leo F. Smith, "Why Students Choose a Particular College," *College and University*, January, 1952, p. 264. (A copy of the questionnaire is included in Appendix 7.)

campus, personal contacts on the campus, publications, paid advertising in newspapers and on radio and television, films and other visual aids, industrial sources, and alumni.

Table 31

RECRUITING TECHNIQUES

| Recruiting technique | Number of institutes utilizing |
|---|---|
| Visits to high schools | 18 |
| Newspaper advertisements | 12 |
| Mailing literature to high schools | 12 |
| Career days or college days | 10 |
| Open house or visiting day | 10 |
| Direct mail advertising | 10 |
| Magazine advertisements | 5 |
| Meetings with high school counselors | 3 |
| Newspaper publicity (not paid advertisement) | 3 |
| Contacts with industry | 3 |
| Advertisements in trade publications | 3 |
| Radio and television advertisements or programs | 3 |
| Field registrars | 1 |
| Mailing student newspaper | 1 |
| Contacts with engineering society | 1 |
| Film about the institute | 1 |
| State fair exhibit | 1 |
| Window displays | 1 |
| High school placards | 1 |
| Sending copies of yearbook to school libraries | 1 |

Off-campus contacts include talking to groups of students at "career days" or "college days," visiting high school counselors or principals, or addressing selected groups of students. Such contacts may be made by a field representative or "field registrar" who devotes his full time to this activity. It is more common in technical institutes, however, for faculty members to make outside contacts on a part-time basis.

Another major area of recruiting activity includes personal contacts on the institute campus. The open house or visiting day is the most popular in this category, and it is not uncommon for 1,000 visitors to be received in a single day. On such occasions exhibits and tours may be arranged and visitors may talk with faculty members. Upon invitation, a high school may send a busload of interested students to visit the institute for an open house. When a technical institute has appropriate curriculums and facilities, a focus for on-campus contacts may be provided by special events and contests in sports, music, debating, journalism, home economics, dramatics, science, business, etc.

In response to the unpublished survey made by the authors in 1954 the Long Island Agricultural and Technical Institute reported that it provides "facilities for meetings of various community, educational, and professional groups." This institute reports that "through such services, plus agricultural and advisory services, the annual Country Life–Open House program, and visits of school children of all ages, we have each year personal contact and relationship with over 100,000 persons of the area."

Publications constitute a third major technique of recruitment. Every technical institute has some type of catalogue or bulletin to describe its courses. Some catalogues can be dull and unattractive in appearance, but if the catalogue is intended to be a promotional device, it can be made attractive and interesting through illustrations, layout, typography, and careful preparation of copy. A common practice is to mail the catalogue to high schools.

Special pamphlets and posters, designed to promote one particular curriculum, are in keeping with the atmosphere and objectives of most technical institutes, and counselors. Career pamphlets are also well adapted for mailing to prospective students or high school guidance counselors. Career pamphlets are also well adapted for technical institutes.[2] They describe a field of work in terms of opportunities, requirements, working conditions, advantages, and disadvantages. These publications may be quite dignified and objective and at the same time promote a curriculum indirectly by arousing interest in that field of study. Unlike a special promotional pamphlet, a career pamphlet may be retained in a high school counselor's occupational file as a basic reference document. Career pamphlets on the engineering technician have been published by the Technical Institute Division of the ASEE[3] and by the Bureau of Labor Statistics.[4] The Na-

[2] In the technical institute field the "Careers in . . ." series of the Rochester Institute of Technology is widely distributed.

[3] *The Engineering Technician,* Technical Institute Division, American Society for Engineering Education, 1953.

[4] *Employment Outlook for Technicians,* Bureau of Labor Statistics Bulletin 1131, Washington, 1953.

tional Council of Technical Schools has also prepared a guidance kit for distribution to high schools.[5]

A number of higher institutions utilize their student newspapers as publicity media. At least two technical institutes mail their student newspapers to prospective students.

Paid advertising in newspapers and magazines and on radio and television is more common in technical institutes than in other college-level institutions. It is important for an institute using advertising to study the impression it wishes to convey to the public and to keep a careful watch on the ethics of the advertising itself.

Some of the best publicity consists of articles or broadcasts about events or activities at the institute. In these presentations the technical institute is likely to have a problem in connection with the accurate interpretation of its character and purposes. A reporter's quick phrase may sometimes convey an inaccurate impression that the institute is either an engineering college, on the one hand, or a trade school, on the other hand. A partial solution to this problem is the employment of a publicity man to write items about the institute, which may be released to the newspapers. The expense of his salary, however, would need to be carefully weighed against other institutional needs.

Oregon Technical Institute and Southern Technical Institute have 16mm sound films which describe the institution in a manner suitable for presentation to high school

[5] National Council of Technical Schools, 912 Seventeenth St., N.W., Washington.

and community audiences. A much cheaper alternative is a filmstrip or a set of slides, with an accompanying narration by an institute representative.

Arousing the interest of prospective students through direct contacts with industry is a recruiting technique which is more readily available to the technical institute than to most institutions The clear-cut occupational focus of each curriculum naturally leads to industrial contacts which can be utilized as sources of students as well as employment outlets for graduates. It is quite common for a young man who has been hired as an apprentice electrician or a machine operator to decide that he would like to improve his chances of advancement by completing a technical institute course. Such a person may often find suitable evening courses, but if he is academically qualified, he may wish to become a daytime student. This is particularly convenient where there is a cooperative plan.

In fields of work where a labor shortage exists, industrial personnel workers sometimes make direct contacts with high schools to recruit for related technical institute programs of study. This approach also is especially logical where there is a cooperative program. Some industrial firms offer scholarships to high school seniors in their geographical area in an effort to attract the more able students to the technical institute courses in which the industry is interested.

Recruiting by industry may be stimulated by the creation of an advisory committee composed of industry representatives who are qualified to advise the institute regarding curriculum content or other aspects of the institute's program. Membership on such a committee promotes mutual understanding and gives industrial personnel workers a greater stake in the recruitment of students.

Among higher institutions generally, some of the best promotion is done by students already at the institution.[6] Graduates are also very effective in the case of technical institutes. Students and graduates tend to engage in informal recruiting activity without any special encouragement by the institution. This informal activity may be supplemented by alumni committees, clubs, or representatives. Sometimes students from the institution are sent individually on visits to their former high schools. Student groups may also make contacts with high schools.

There are interesting differences between institutions in attitudes toward publicity and recruiting. Several of the institutes state that they utilize any device they can think of to bring their programs to the attention of prospective students. On the other hand, at least two institutes severely limit their recruiting activities. The Long Island Agricultural and Technical Institute at Farmingdale does "not practice recruiting of students in the sense of personal solicitation, either of individuals or of high school principals—we go where we are invited if the place is within our natural service area." The New York City Community College of Applied Arts and Sciences at Brooklyn reports, "we do everything possible to avoid proselytizing and are interested in receiving applications only from those who are intent upon, and can profit best by, our form of two-year terminal technical education."

[6] W. Emerson Reck, editor, *College Publicity Manual,* Harper & Brothers, New York, 1948, p. 156.

## What recruiting techniques are most successful?

The 1954 survey by the authors asked technical institutes to list the recruiting techniques which they found most successful. Table 32 gives the results.

TABLE 32

SUCCESS OF RECRUITING TECHNIQUES

| Recruiting technique | Number of institutes finding most successful |
|---|---|
| Recommendations of graduates | 15 |
| Visits to high schools | 6 |
| Radio and television programs | 3 |
| Direct mail | 2 |
| Newspaper advertisements | 2 |
| Contacts with high school counselors | 2 |
| Personal contacts | 2 |
| Sending literature in answer to inquiries | 1 |
| Illustrated talks on visits to high schools | 1 |

In attempting to evaluate the relative effectiveness of its several publicity media, the technical institute division of the Pennsylvania State University conducted a survey to determine "how the student first learned of the technical institute program." For full-time day students, the ranking of media was as follows:[7]

1. Newspaper advertising
2. Word of mouth (former students, counselors, etc.)
3. Direct mail

[7] Technical Institute Committee Report submitted at the annual meeting of the National University Extension Association, University of Texas, May, 1952.

4. Radio
5. Newspaper stories
6. Window display
7. Placards
8. Miscellaneous

The Aeronautical University reports that 38 per cent of the student body is recruited through the activities of graduates. The Rochester Institute of Technology found that 34 per cent of its freshmen first heard about the Institute through a graduate or student and that high school principals, counselors, and teachers accounted for an additional 22 per cent.

## Admissions

No technical institute undertakes to serve the needs of all types of potential students or all occupational fields. Selective admission of students who can profit from its courses is more important for the technical institute than for most institutions. The short duration and specific goals of technical institute programs make them suitable only for students who have made a vocational choice and who have appropriate ability and preparation.

Self-selection by prospective students is by far the most significant aspect of the selection process for technical institutes. Students who choose technical institute programs of study typically become interested in a particular occupational field and then look for an institution where they can prepare for this type of work. As students examine technical institute offerings, there is a tendency to match their own aptitudes and abilities with curricular requirements. As a result, a very high percentage of applicants meet the requirements for admission and for successful completion of the courses of study.

Self-selection, however, cannot be depended upon as the sole criterion for admission. A technical institute has responsibilities to students, faculty, and financial supporters to admit to its courses only those applicants who have a reasonable chance of success. A scientific approach to the selective admission of students involves several steps which can be clearly defined but which are difficult to accomplish. It is doubtful if any institution—technical institute, college, or university—has completed these steps to the fullest possible extent. Basic steps in a scientific approach to the selective admission of technical institute students are:

1. Determine the characteristics believed to be necessary for success in the institute program, on the job, and as a citizen.
2. Canvass the methods of identifying the characteristics which are found to be important. This may involve:
   *a.* High school transcript
   *b.* Personal data blank
   *c.* Personal interview
   *d.* Tests
3. Develop adequate measures of success in the institute programs. This involves suitable examinations and grading procedures.
4. Select or construct blanks, tests, or other devices designed to identify the characteristics which are found to be important.
5. Determine what relationships, if any, exist between the information obtained (such as test scores) and the measures of

success in institute courses and criteria of other important characteristics.

6. According to the degree of statistical relationship found, set appropriate standards in terms of test scores or other data.
7. Make a periodic reevaluation of the selection devices by repeating the foregoing steps.

A number of institutions which have not thoroughly completed all of the foregoing steps nevertheless have low drop-out rates and a record of successful placement of graduates. Part of this success may be attributed to self-selection by prospective students. A successful admissions program may also reflect the judgment and skill of an experienced interviewer.

The admission requirements most frequently set by technical institutes include

1. High school graduation.
2. Completion of certain high school subjects.
3. Satisfactory scores on entrance tests.
4. Qualifications of character and personality.

Among the commonly required high school subjects are elementary algebra, plane geometry, and physics. Some institutes require the completion of as much as two-and-one-half years of high school mathematics.

In the authors' survey of technical institutes in 1954, several questions were asked about admissions policies. Of thirty-five institutes responding to these questions, twenty-nine require high school graduation or a high school equivalency diploma for entrance. Six institutes do not require a high school diploma.

Seventeen institutes reported that they used psychological tests prior to admission, and seventeen stated that they did not. Of the institutes utilizing tests, two administer tests only in certain cases. In 1951, the Committee on Counseling and Guidance of the Technical Institute Division of the ASEE sent questionnaires to sixty-nine technical institutes in a survey of several aspects of student personnel services. Of the forty-three institutions which replied, the tests administered to prospective students before entrance were as follows:

| Type of test | Number of institutes |
|---|---|
| Mental ability | 4 |
| Interest | 3 |
| Aptitudes | 21 |
| Achievement | 8 |
| Personality | 5 |

Several technical institutes use the American Council on Education Psychological Examination as an entrance test. At one state institute, 149 students were enrolled in five different technological curriculums in 1953. In comparison with the national norms for college freshmen, the scores of these institute students ranged from the 1st to the 90th percentile. The median was approximately at the 50th percentile. At this same institute 14 students cooperatively employed by one industrial firm had ACE test scores ranging from the 59th to the 90th percentile.

In one of the older privately endowed institutes freshmen entered three technological curriculums in 1953. Their raw scores on the 1949 edition of the ACE test ranged from 78 to 154, or from the 16th to the 98th percentiles on the national norms. The median score of 113 would fall at the 64th percentile on the national norms for college freshmen.

The records of an accredited proprietary technical institute, showed that the 85 freshmen who entered in 1952 had IQs on the Otis Gamma test ranging from 81 to 129, with a median of 106.

In the 1954 survey, seven of the forty responding institutes reported that they have established minimum test scores for admission. The specific cutoff scores reported were:

1. 25th percentile on ACE Psychological Examination.
2. IQ of 108 for ECPD-accredited courses.
3. Otis IQ of 90.
4. "C" on Detroit Mechanical Aptitude Test.
5. Survey of Mechanical Insight, 30th percentile on Grade 10 norms, and Progressive Mathematics Test, 40th percentile on Grade 10 norms.

Two institutes reported that they had certain minimum scores in mind but that these were not absolute and were considered in light of the applicant's complete record. Several institutes reported that they are currently accumulating data which they hope may enable them to establish minimum scores on entrance tests.

Only two of the forty institutes responding to the 1954 survey insist upon any particular standing in the applicant's high school class. Although no specific question about preadmission interviews was asked in the 1954 survey, several institutes volunteered the information that an interview is required. Interview impressions alone would seldom cause the rejection of a student, but an interview may be utilized for the following purposes:

1. To obtain a rough estimate of ultimate employability in the student's chosen field.

2. To impart information for the student's guidance and orientation.

3. To obtain guidance and placement information regarding motivation, goals, personality characteristics, interests, special needs, finances, etc.

In summarizing admissions policy, one state-supported institute stated that no fixed standing in the high school class or specific test scores are required. "Personal interview, experience, background, objectives, and estimates of adaptability to the desired training all come into the picture."

## Summary

Technical institutes have usually found that students enroll because of their interest in a specific course of study leading to a well-defined occupational goal. Most institutes carry on active public relations and recruiting programs, utilizing a wide variety of devices and activities. The recruiting techniques which the institutes believe to be most successful are recommendations of graduates, visits to high schools by institute staff members, radio and television programs, direct mail, newspaper advertisements, contacts with high school counselors, and various personal contacts with prospective students.

Self-selection by prospective students is particularly important in determining who will enroll in a technical institute. In addition, many technical institutes are taking significant steps toward the development of scientific procedures for admitting only those students who have a good chance to succeed. In most institutes high school graduation is a requirement for admission, and the completion of certain high school subjects is frequently required. Psychological tests are administered by a number of institutes before students are admitted, and in five institutes certain scores on these tests have been set as minimum requirements for admission. More often, however, admission is based upon a combination of factors, including high school record, test scores, and interview impressions of the applicant's experience, maturity, objectives, and motivation.

CHAPTER 11

# Student Personnel Services

In the early days of technical institute development, occupational needs, rather narrowly defined, were the only ones which the institute attempted to meet. Over the years, however, social, educational, and philosophical developments have broadened the conception of occupational needs and have brought other needs to the attention of technical institute educators.[1]

[1] C. Gilbert Wrenn, *Student Personnel Work in College,* The Ronald Press Company, New York, 1951, p. 8, cites the following needs of young people between the ages of twelve and twenty:

1. The need to become increasingly independent of parents and other adults.
2. The need to establish satisfying intellectual, social, and emotional relations with the opposite sex.
3. The need for status in his own age group, acceptance by both sexes.
4. The need for a sense of security: emotional security in having someone love him and believe in him, economic security in the present with promise for the future, social security in the sense of belonging to an accepted social unit, such as the family or other primary social group.
5. The need for success and a feeling of growth or achievement

As institutes have broadened their objectives in accordance with broadening conceptions of human needs, they have moved toward the objective of educating the *whole* student in a unified program designed not only to provide vocational competence but also to bring about individual and social development in a much broader sense.

Within the last three decades, professional specialties within the field of student personnel work have developed to break down into manageable proportions the various services which attempt to meet the needs of students outside the classroom. These areas of student personnel work may be classified as follows:[2]

1. Admissions.
2. Orientation.
3. Housing and food service.
4. Health services.
5. Counseling.
6. Remedial services (reading, speech, study habits).
7. Student activities.
8. Financial aids and student employment.
9. Job-placement service.
10. Cumulative personnel records.

It is the purpose of this chapter to outline the major principles and practices under these headings which are most important for technical institutes. Readers with specific interests or responsibilities in connection with stu-

---

in at least one area of his life.

6. The need for an acceptable goal for the future, both vocational goal and life purpose.

[2] Cf. Wrenn, *op. cit.,* p. 24.

dent personnel work are referred to the considerable body of literature in this field.[3-11]

## Admissions

The principles and practices of technical institute admissions have been discussed in the previous chapter. At this point it is important to mention the importance of admissions in an integrated student personnel program. To the extent that selective admissions principles are followed, a considerable amount of information about the student is obtained before he enrolls. Much of the value of this information is lost unless the relevant material is passed along to the individuals responsible for counseling. Weaknesses in the student's high school preparation may be met through remedial programs, social needs may be filled by encouraging the student to participate in certain

[3] Dugald S. Arbuckle, *Student Personnel Services in Higher Education,* McGraw-Hill Book Company, Inc., New York, 1953.

[4] Paul J. Brouwer, *Student Personnel Services in General Education,* American Council on Education, Washington, 1949.

[5] Esther Lloyd-Jones, *A Student Personnel Program for Higher Education,* McGraw-Hill Book Company, Inc., New York, 1938.

[6] Anna Y. Reed, *Guidance and Personnel Services in Education.* Cornell University Press, Ithaca, 1944.

[7] John Dale Russell, *Student Personnel Services in Colleges and Universities.* University of Chicago Press, Chicago, 1941.

[8] *The Student Personnel Point of View,* American Council on Education, Washington, 1949.

[9] *Student Personnel Programs in Transition,* American Council on Education, Washington, 1952.

[10] E. G. Williamson, ed., *Trends in Student Personnel Work.* University of Minnesota Press, Minneapolis, 1949.

[11] Wrenn, *op. cit.*

student activities, medical service may be provided for health problems, financial aids may be provided, and counseling may be planned to assist the student in dealing with personal problems. To a considerable extent, admissions policies determine the needs of the institute in terms of other personnel services and information obtained in the admissions process is the foundation of a program in which personnel services will be utilized to help each student reach his maximum achievement.

## Orientation

Ruth Strang defines orientation to collegiate-level institutions as "assisting students in acquiring techniques of living in college, in achieving a beneficial balance among all the demands and opportunities of college life, and in gaining perspective and a sense of purpose."[12] This may include acquainting students with the buildings and grounds, with health, recreational, and counseling facilities, with traditions and regulations, and with the curriculum itself.

Orientation properly begins before the student is admitted. Most of the publicity devices mentioned in Chapter 6 have orientation values. This is particularly true of the catalogue, the open house, and correspondence.

The size and nature of most technical institutes eliminate the need for the elaborate orientation procedures necessary in large universities, but several institutes set aside a day or two for orientation before classes begin. This period may be used for lectures, assemblies, campus

[12] *Ibid.*, p. 274.

tours, and social functions, which help the student become adjusted to his environment. In collegiate institutions generally the "trend is toward expecting less of the 'Freshman Days' and extending the process over a semester."[13]

In the area of occupational orientation, the technical institute has a unique problem and responsibility. It is particularly important for the technical institute student to verify the suitability of his vocational choice, to select a specific job goal within his field of study, and to develop attitudes which will make him an effective employee immediately after graduation. Cooperative employment is probably the best method of occupational orientation available to the technical institute because it provides the most intimate and realistic acquaintance with the field of work for which the student is preparing.

## Housing and food service

Technical institutes have had a less acute problem in respect to student residence halls than have other collegiate-level institutions. In the first place, most technical institutes have a high percentage of students who live at home. In the second place, most institutes are located in urban centers where private housing is more readily available than in the typical college town.

[13] *Ibid.*, p. 282. Continuing orientation activities may include meetings of dormitory residents; other group meetings, with faculty or upperclass students' participation; lectures by the medical staff, registrar, counselors, and other student personnel workers; teas or other meetings for freshmen conducted by various campus organizations. Some institutions have upperclass students as counselors for freshmen.

A very important phase of a student's total educational program can be developed through institutional housing.[14] The principal types of student housing are dormitories, private off-campus rooming houses, fraternity and sorority houses, and cooperative houses. A choice by a technical institute depends on several factors including

1. The institute's objectives, especially in terms of general education.
2. The extent to which housing is considered a suitable medium for the achievement of educational objectives.
3. Number of students needing housing.
4. Available facilities.
5. Financial resources of students.
6. Financing plans available to the institute.
7. Stability of enrollment.

In connection with a choice of type of housing, there is general agreement among student personnel workers on the following basic principles:

1. Living in a dormitory is associated with better grades, while living in a fraternity house favors participation in student activities.[15]
2. Small living units are desirable.
3. Most problems of group living can be handled most effectively through self-government.[16]

[14] Mary Medden, "Apartment Life," *College and Business*, February, 1949.

[15] Wrenn, *op. cit.*, p. 295.

[16] Florence M. Thompson, "Residence Halls and the Educational Program," *Educ. Rec.*, vol. 29, pp. 64–71, January, 1948.

Selection of the type of food service and dining facilities which the technical institute should provide depends upon the same factors as those which determine the type of housing. Dining halls can provide practice in social skills. Budgeting, purchasing, and even cooking in a fraternity house or cooperative house can provide other valuable educational experiences for students. Even eating in restaurants may be a useful experience for the less sophisticated students. The food service provided by an institute is a particularly important factor in determining student expenses and student morale.

## Health services

Health services, like other elements of a technical institute program, develop to meet institutional objectives. Possible objectives relating to health services include:

1. Selective admission of students who are physically and mentally able to undertake the institute's program.

2. Identification of physical characteristics or health problems of admissible students which may be remedied or improved during the students' stay at the institute.

3. Treating illnesses and injuries of enrolled students.

4. Taking positive steps to improve the health and well-being of students.

5. Maintaining a sanitary environment, including measures designed to prevent health problems.

In general, health services have tended to develop more slowly in technical institutes than in other types of higher institutions. This is probably because institutes have usually selected a relatively limited set of objectives, with emphasis on the occupational. Size of enrollment may be another factor. Many technical institute catalogues make no mention of any medical services whatsoever, although even these institutions are likely to have first-aid facilities and opportunities for referral to physicians or hospitals. The catalogue of one proprietary institute states: "Affiliations are established by the school with several excellent medical centers, and prompt emergency treatment is available."

As technical institutes have broadened their objectives to include more interest in the whole student, there has been a tendency to increase medical services. One endowed technical institute maintains a full-time nurse, and a physician is employed for a one-hour consulting period on each day that school is in session.[17]

Technical institutes, like other institutions, often lack the staff, funds, and facilities to provide all the medical services which would be desirable. One solution for this

[17] This may be compared with the medical services in a college with an enrollment of 2,500 to 3,000 men, which provides (1) a comprehensive health examination for entering students, including an interview to discuss the student's health status and ways to correct any defects; (2) routine examinations for all students once a year, for athletes before contests, for physically handicapped students at least twice a year, to seniors before graduation; (3) control of contagious diseases; (4) modification of the programs of physically handicapped students; (5) referral to the dean's office for counseling of students having physical conditions that may limit academic achievement; (6) first aid; (7) ultraviolet treatment for those who need it. Cf. Frederik A. Olsen, "Health Service to College Men," *J. Hlth. Phys. Educ.*, vol. 16, p. 236, May, 1945.

problem in connection with entrance examinations is the requirement that each applicant submit a report of a physical examination by his own physician. Another is the employment of a part-time physician or nurse rather than a full-time medical worker. In some instances it may be possible to arrange for medical services in local hospitals. Group health-insurance plans have been increasing in technical institutes, as well as in colleges and universities. Under such plans a modest fee, separate from tuition, may be charged each student for comprehensive health services.

## Counseling

Where an educational institution undertakes to meet the needs of the whole student, needs are recognized which can be dealt with only through individual contacts with students. Many of these contacts fall under the heading of counseling, if the term is defined broadly. "Counseling is a dynamic and purposeful relationship between two people in which procedures vary with the nature of the student's need but in which there is always mutual participation by counselor and student with the focus upon self-clarification and self-determination by the student."[18]

There are many specialized disciplines within the general field of counseling, and a complete coverage of this subject is far beyond the scope of this book.[19] Those who

[18] Wrenn, *op. cit.,* p. 60.

[19] Counselors with various training and interests may designate themselves as vocational, therapeutic or clinical, religious, marriage, educational, etc.

wish to pursue the subject further are referred to the large body of professional literature in the counseling field.[20-24]

The counseling needs of a technical institute may be considered from the standpoint of levels of intensity and complexity of counseling.[25] One level of counseling contact includes various casual relationships between students on the one hand and faculty and staff on the other. This may involve students' questions about facilities, schedules, and the like.

Counseling at a second level is performed by designated individuals, who may be called "advisers," regarding courses, requirements, study techniques, student organizations, and facilities. This second level of counseling requires knowledge of the relevant facts, but it does not ordinarily require any special training in the process of counseling.

For a third level of counseling, members of the faculty are carefully selected on the basis of interest, personal qualifications, and perhaps some training in counseling. Such individuals may be relieved of a percentage of their teaching or administrative duties so that they may have

[20] Ralph F. Berdie, *Concepts and Programs of Counseling*, University of Minnesota Press, Minneapolis, 1951.

[21] Arthur H. Brayfield, *Readings in Modern Methods of Counseling*, Appleton-Century-Crofts, Inc., New York, 1950.

[22] William J. Reilly, *Life Planning for College Students*, Harper & Brothers, New York, 1954.

[23] Carl R. Rogers, *Client-centered Therapy*, Houghton Mifflin Company, Boston, 1951.

[24] Wrenn, *op. cit.*

[25] *Ibid.*, pp. 68–70.

time for more intensive counseling of students. This may involve personal problems with more emotional content than the matters handled by an adviser. Most technical institutions could recruit or train individuals who would be competent at this third level. In fact, this is the type of counseling most readily available in technical institutes.

Counseling at a fourth level is done by fully trained workers, such as psychologists or vocational counselors, who spend all or most of their professional time in this field. At this level there is responsibility, time, and training for studying the needs of an individual student as thoroughly as necessary and for administering therapy. This type of fully trained counselor may use psychological tests in diagnostic procedures. Although full-time professional counselors are employed in few technical institutes at present, their number is increasing.

With extremely disturbed or psychotic individuals, the services of a psychiatrist are necessary. The medical staffs of the larger universities include psychiatrists, but no technical institute up to this time has required the services of a full-time psychiatrist. Where necessary, psychiatric service is made available to students on a referral basis.

In 1951 a survey of forty-three technical institutes by the committee on counseling and guidance of the Technical Institute Division of the ASEE found that ten of these institutes had full-time guidance or student personnel directors. Department heads were mentioned most frequently as the individuals responsible for counseling. Another widespread practice was counseling by instructors, either informally or as a regular assignment. Two of the forty-three institutes maintained counseling centers, and one utilized student counselors.

The 1954 survey, covering forty institutes, obtained the thirty-six responses given in Table 33 in answer to a question about the type of counseling services available.

TABLE 33

COUNSELING IN TECHNICAL INSTITUTES

| Primary type of counseling resource | Number of institutes |
|---|---|
| Special counselors (part-time or full-time) | 10 |
| Assignment of each student to a faculty adviser (supplemented by specialists in four institutes) | 7 |
| No definite plan—student initiates contacts with any faculty or staff member of his choice | 7 |
| Counseling primarily by top administrators | 5 |
| Counseling primarily by department heads | 4 |
| Combination of department heads and regular faculty members | 3 |

Although none of the institutes responding to the surveys mentioned the use of off-campus agencies, these represent a resource which may be particularly useful for the smaller institutes. YMCAs, psychological counseling services, vocational guidance agencies, social agencies, psychiatric services, and diagnostic or therapeutic clinics are found in most large cities. The technical institute student who lives at home can benefit especially from acquaintance with these services in his community.

The 1951 survey by the Committee on Counseling and Guidance found that psychological tests were in fairly widespread use as diagnostic tools in connection with counseling. Fifty-seven different tests were used by the forty-three institutions. In the area of mental ability, the Otis Self-Administering Tests of Mental Ability, the ACE Psychological Examination, and the Differential Aptitude Tests were used most frequently. The Kuder Preference Record was the most widely used device in the field of interests. In the area of special aptitudes, the tests used most commonly by the institutes were the Engineering and Physical Science Aptitude Test, the Minnesota Paper Form Board, and the Bennett Test of Mechanical Comprehension.

### Remedial services

There would be no need for remedial services in higher education if admissions procedures selected only the students who were fully qualified for all courses and who had no remedial defects. There is no technical institute, however, where enrollment is so limited. When students have academic or other difficulties of a remediable nature, there is a choice between letting the student drop out and providing special help for him. Few institutes would fail to provide such special help within the limits of their capacity.

One of the areas of study most likely to require special remedial assistance for some technical institute students is reading. Many students complete high school without attaining adequate reading speed and comprehension for college-level study. In a technical institute a large percentage of what the student learns comes through reading.

Academic problems may often be traced to a handicap in this skill.

The first step in meeting such a problem is to identify it. This may be done through English classes or testing by personnel specialists. For actual remedial instruction there are several possibilities.

A number of colleges and universities now have special courses for the development of reading skill. Some of these institutions also have clinics with special apparatus where students come individually for individual instruction or practice. Both of these approaches are open to any technical institute which wishes to provide a budget for these services. At least one technical institute has remedial reading equipment and specially trained instructors whose schedules are relieved of a percentage of their other duties.

In the smaller or less affluent technical institutes, however, this expense may not be justified. A more practical approach may be to provide certain individualized instruction within the regular English classes.

Mathematics is another area which may require remedial service. Passing certain high school subjects does not guarantee ability to cope with technical institute mathematics courses. In this field there is no established need for special equipment or for specialists other than regular mathematics teachers. The principal problem is in scheduling to allow students time for special instruction without missing their regular assignments.

Remedial services may also be needed in a technical institute in the field of study habits and techniques. In some instances these may be dealt with in individual counseling, and it is likely that a counseling approach would be required to identify a study problem. In some instances, special classes may be set up or special emphasis placed on study methods in connection with regular curricular work.

There are other remedial services, such as speech therapy, which are required by only a very small number of students. Most technical institutes presently find it more practicable to refer such problems to outside agencies than to provide their own clinics or specialists.

If the principle is accepted that a technical institute should provide each enrollee with the services necessary to enable him to reach the objectives of his program, the following steps are indicated:

1. Provide selection procedures which eliminate students for whom the institute is unable or unwilling to furnish all the necessary services.
2. Set up procedures for identification of problems which may require special assistance.
3. Provide whatever services are indicated by the problems which are identified. This may require the advice of various professional specialists.

### Student activities

Some educational institutions plan their programs on the assumption that formal education involves only intellectual activity which is unrelated to other aspects of living. However, there is a mass of evidence that learning within the classroom is significantly affected by outside influences upon the student. In addition, a student spends more of his waking hours outside the classroom than in it.

In short, extracurricular activities cannot be ignored, even in the case of institutions with narrowly defined objectives.

Increasingly, technical institutes are broadening their objectives to include not only vocational goals but also the social and personal development of the student. The achievement of such objectives *requires* utilization of extracurricular activities. Student activities represent an educational resource which may be fully as important as classroom and laboratory experiences. The key steps in planning student activities are:

1. Determine the objectives.
2. Canvass the various kinds of experiences which might contribute to the achievement of these objectives.
3. Plan a balanced program of activities.
4. Evaluate the program periodically and modify it if necessary.

Some of the objectives which may be achieved through extracurricular activities include developing skill in human relations and leadership, deepening understanding of the democratic process, maintaining or improving physical and mental health, providing satisfying relationships with the opposite sex, developing "school spirit," providing experiences for aesthetic appreciation, learning sportsmanship, and promoting mutual understanding between students and faculty.

Examples of student activities in technical institutes include varsity and intramural athletics, fraternities and sororities, religious clubs, publications, clubs for such sports as swimming and skiing, and dramatic and musical groups.

Many student activities are most effective when they are organized by the students themselves. Student self-government may provide a particularly useful medium for achieving some of the foregoing objectives. It may also provide the best means of keeping student activities abreast of student needs. Technical institutes, with their strong vocational emphasis, have not yet developed student government activities on the scale found at Antioch and Goddard Colleges, but many institutes have well-developed student councils. In one technical institute, the student council determines the amount of student fees and administers these funds for athletics, lounges, social events, clubs, and other student activities.[26] This responsibility and authority derive from a constitutional grant of power from the administration.

### Financial aids and student employment

A substantial number of students with the interests and abilities necessary for success in a technical institute lack the financial resources needed to complete a program of study. A technical institute which attempts to serve students with limited funds must provide some type of financial assistance. The principal types of financial aid which are available to the technical institute are:

1. *Scholarships.* These are outright grants which usually consist of all or part of tuition. Scholarship funds may be derived from (*a*) the general resources of the institute; (*b*) industrial firms which may wish to sponsor certain

[26] Burton E. Stratton, "Students Can Govern Themselves," *Educ. Admin. Supervis.*, April, 1941, pp. 291–295.

students or programs; (*c*) other sources available to the student, such as the funds of religious, fraternal, and civic groups.

2. *Loans.* These may come from funds set aside by the institute or from outside sources.

3. *Student employment.* Most institutions find it possible to employ students in clerical positions, food services, building and grounds work, laboratory jobs, and other types of work.

4. *Cooperative houses.* By sharing the work in eating or housing, students may cut expenses considerably. Cooperatives are usually student-operated, but they may require some supervision or subsidy from the institution.

5. *Cooperative work programs.* Described more fully in Chapter 12, cooperative employment in industry provides not only educational values but also an important financial resource.

Determining which students shall receive financial aids is a problem deserving careful study. Awards are usually based upon one or more of the following criteria:

1. Scholastic standing and ability.
2. Financial need.
3. Character and personality.

The relative importance of these criteria is determined by the objectives of a financial aid program. In other words, does the institution wish to use this means to attract students of outstanding scholarship? Or does it primarily wish to make education available to greater numbers of average students with limited financial resources?

Whatever criteria are considered most important may

well be applied to all financial aids administered by the institute, including student employment. A broad look at the financial aid program makes it possible to award the type of aid "which will contribute most to that particular student's development."[27] For example, a student who needs to spend more than the average amount of time studying may profit most from an outright scholarship grant. On the other hand, a quick-thinking student who lacks work experience may gain most from a campus job.

Procedures for the selection of students who shall receive financial aid depend upon the criteria considered most important. Development of these procedures deserves careful study and an examination of sources which discuss the principles of financial aids more thoroughly than is possible in this book.[28-30]

## Job-placement service

One of the primary aims of a technical institute is to prepare graduates for clear-cut occupational fields. This objective cannot be achieved unless graduates are suitably placed. Placement services are designed to bring together students, potential employers, and information valuable to both. They refer students to jobs and introduce employers to qualified students. To be effective, a placement director must have extensive contacts with persons who

[27] Wrenn, *op. cit.*, p. 363.

[28] Margaret R. Smith, *Student Aid*, Columbia University Press, New York, 1937.

[29] Russell T. Sharpe *et al.*, *Financial Assistance for College Students*, American Council on Education, Washington, 1946.

[30] Wrenn, *op. cit.*

are potential employers of institute graduates, he must provide appropriate occupational information for students, and he must provide prospective employers with suitable information about graduating students. Through knowledge of courses, personality factors, and job situations, he can assist both students and employers to achieve suitable placements.

In many instances student activities and learning experiences gained from residence-hall life or from student employment will have an important bearing upon job placement possibilities. Leadership skills, for example, are a marketable asset in industry. However, the utilization of both classroom and out-of-class experiences in placement can be effective only to the extent that appropriate records are available.

The most debated problem in connection with institutional placement is that of centralization. Some of the advantages of a central placement office are:

1. Employers have a central reference point for all inquiries and visits.
2. Specialization by one individual or staff may lead to more effective and more professional practices.
3. Placement opportunities for all students are theoretically equalized.

Some problems or disadvantages in connection with central placement are:

1. One placement director's contacts with many employers may be less intimate and less effective than those of a faculty member or department head with fewer employers.

2. Central records make procedures more complicated.

3. In some instances placement is facilitated by specialized knowledge of the industry.

To combine the advantages of both centralized and decentralized placement, Wrenn[31] suggests a compromise plan:

1. Centralization of all job referrals and employer visits.

2. Centralization of all student registrations.

3. Decentralization of actual placement to the extent that a department or faculty member has special interest or ability in this connection.

Technical institutes having programs of cooperative employment have an important placement advantage arising from the fact that a large percentage of students will remain with their cooperative employers after graduation. The cooperative plan presents special problems, however, because of the intimate relationship between cooperative job and educational program.

It is not the purpose of this section to outline in detail all of the activities of a technical institute placement office.[32-35] It should be emphasized, however, that place-

[31] *Ibid.*, p. 396.

[32] R. F. Chambers, *College Placement: Philosophy, Organization, Techniques and Procedures,* University of Colorado, Boulder, 1952.

[33] F. H. Kirkpatrick, *et al.*, *Helping Students Find Employment,* American Council on Education, Washington, 1949.

[34] N. A. Johnson, "Integrating Placement with the Student Personnel Program," *Educational and Psychological Measurement,* vol. 9, no. 3, pp. 602–613, 1949.

[35] L. L. Boykin and H. A. Bowen, "Placement Services, Practices

ment is a particularly important activity of a technical institute because it represents in many ways the culmination of the total institute program.

**Cumulative student personnel records**

"Cumulative personnel records are an outward and visible sign of the school's desire to understand the individual student."[36] It is obvious that many of the student personnel activities described in this chapter may result in records. It is equally obvious that recorded information about a student will be helpful, if not essential, in counseling, remedial services, placement, and other contacts with the same student.

The specific information which is included in student personnel records will depend upon the objectives of the institution and of the student personnel program. Typical items which would be included in comprehensive cumulative records include preadmission correspondence and information, high school transcript and references, entrance test scores, academic grades, notes from counseling and health service contacts (except for items which may be too confidential for the general files), records of financial aid and student employment, records of any remedial services, and anecdotes from faculty members and others who have significant contacts with the student. "Ideally, all of the information that is available about any given student should be available at one time and place in any

---

and Responsibilities in American Colleges and Universities," *Coll. Univer.*, vol. 24, pp. 346–357, April, 1949.

[36] Ruth Strang, *Counseling Technics in College and Secondary School*, Harper & Brothers, New York, 1949, p. 180.

type of personal adjustment or planning contacts with that student."[37]

This information might be in the files of a faculty adviser, department head, registrar, or dean. In a small institution, one file for each student may suffice. In a larger institution, however, several different individuals may have use for a student's comprehensive record. This problem can be solved by duplication of all or part of the record information. Modern methods of duplicating are making such a practice increasingly convenient and inexpensive.

In connection with the development and maintenance of cumulative student personnel records, the following principles are suggested:

1. Records serve the purposes of the institution and flow only from its objectives.
2. Information has a place in cumulative records only to the extent that there is a plan for its use.
3. All persons who utilize cumulative records extensively have a potential contribution to make regarding the form and content of the records.
4. Principles of simplification and eye appeal are as important in connection with personnel records as in other paper work.

## Summary

The objective of occupational competence was the only important objective with which most of the early technical institutes were concerned, but there is an increasing tendency to broaden objectives in the direction

[37] Wrenn, *op. cit.,* p. 437.

of individual and social development. To a considerable extent it is necessary to utilize experiences outside the classroom as a means of attaining nonoccupational objectives. Out-of-class activities may also make an important contribution to the curriculum by contributing to the physical and mental health of the students and to their readiness for learning.

An institution's out-of-class services for the benefit of students have come to be known as student personnel services, which may be classified under the following headings: admissions, orientation, housing and food service, health services, counseling, remedial services, student activities, financial aids, job placement, and cumulative personnel records.

In recent years professional specialists have developed in each of these areas. Achieving balance and coordination in the development of student personnel services is a difficult task, which few institutes have accomplished to the best possible extent, although great strides have been made.

Like classroom instruction, student personnel services are most effective when they are carefully and systematically planned. This approach involves

1. Determining the objectives to be served.
2. Canvassing the various means of attaining these objectives.
3. Planning appropriate services and activities, utilizing any expert consultation that may be required.
4. Evaluating the effectiveness of the program and making any improvements that may be indicated.

CHAPTER 12

# Cooperative Education

The concept of learning by doing is accepted in principle by many educators as a desirable technique. In practice, however, this philosophy has not always been carried out. One type of education which seems particularly well adapted to technical institutes and technical-terminal programs is cooperative education or the cooperative work program (terms which will be used synonymously throughout this chapter).

Although the term "cooperative" has many meanings in education, the meaning which will be employed in this chapter is as follows:[1]

> By cooperative education or cooperative work program is meant that type of curriculum which includes alternation of regularly scheduled instructional periods in school and periods of employment in business or industry with definite provision for integrating work experience into the total education of the student.

[1] Leo F. Smith, *Cooperative Work Programs in Higher Institutions,* unpublished Ph.D. dissertation, University of Chicago, 1943, p. 4.

This definition was formulated in 1941 by a committee of six faculty members at the Rochester Institute of Technology with a total of more than fifty years of experience in cooperative education. There are several features of the foregoing definition which are worthy of note:

1. It is broad enough to include cooperative programs in which work is looked upon as a broadening educational experience and the particular job held does not have to be closely related to the student's major field of study.
2. It states that provisions should be made for planned periods of alternation between school and work and coordination of the theoretical and practical experience.
3. It is applicable to programs at all levels of education.
4. It is not so broad that it includes all types of part-time work and odd jobs which the majority of students engage in at some time during their school life.

## History of cooperative education

In the United States the cooperative plan of education originated with the late Dean Herman Schneider, who put it into operation at the University of Cincinnati in 1906. Prior to that time, there had been criticisms of the training offered by the engineering schools because it appeared that there was a definite lack of effort to relate the theory taught in school with actual practices carried on in industry.

A possible solution to this problem came to Professor Schneider while he was employed at one of the large eastern universities:[2]

[2] Clyde W. Park, *The Cooperative System of Education,* U.S. Bureau of Education Bulletin 37, Washington, 1916, p. 7.

> One evening as he was walking across the campus of an eastern university where he was teaching, he heard the answer in the blast of a Bessemer furnace at a neighboring steel plant. Instantly the idea appealed to him as perfectly simple and obvious. Here was something better than any conceivable school shop—a million dollar laboratory with unlimited possibilities for illustrating the applications of technical theory. In this plant many graduates of the same college would find employment, as others had done before them. Why should they not learn as students to translate their book knowledge into terms of industrial processes?

The idea was not enthusiastically received by the traditionally minded faculty of that institution and it was not until several years later, after he had accepted a position in the engineering department at the University of Cincinnati, that he had the opportunity to put his idea into action.

Following the inception of the program at Cincinnati in 1906, the cooperative plan has had a slow but wholesome growth in colleges and universities, technical institutes and junior colleges. In the study[3] carried on for the Commission on Terminal Education of the American Association of Junior Colleges, a total of twenty-nine colleges and universities, four technical institutes, and thirty-three junior colleges were found which offered cooperative programs during the school year 1941–1942.

In 1953–1954 Armsby[4] found that there were thirty-

[3] Smith, *op. cit.*, pp. 170–175.

[4] H. H. Armsby, *Cooperative Education in the United States,* U.S. Department of Health, Education, and Welfare Bulletin 11, Washington, 1954. This bulletin presents an organized outline of the

five colleges and universities and eight technical institutes offering cooperative work programs. He did not study the number of programs offered in junior colleges.

In 1946 the Cooperative Engineering Education Division of the ASEE adopted a report[5] which had been prepared by the Committee on Aims and Ideals of Cooperative Engineering Education as the official statement of policy for the Division. Readers interested in more specific aspects of cooperative education are referred to this comprehensive document.

## Cooperative work programs

The cooperative plan seems particularly well-suited to technical institute programs. In fact, as far back as 1931 the following statement was made by Wickenden and Spahr:[6]

> The cooperative plan, based on alternating periods of school work and industrial employment, seems particularly well adapted to the aims and the levels of age and work of the technical institutes. The plan has marked advantages in the training of supervisors of production, operation and maintenance. . . . It affords the student a valid trial of aptitude and a normal orientation to industry without necessitating a break in the continuity of education. The coopera-

---

basic philosophy and objectives of cooperative education, its administrative problems, its presents status, and its values to the student, institution, and employer.

[5] C. J. Freund, "The Cooperative System—A Manifesto," *J. Engng. Educ.*, vol. 37, pp. 117–134, October, 1946.

[6] William E. Wickenden and Robert H. Spahr, *A Study of Technical Institutes*, Society for the Promotion of Engineering Education, Lancaster, Pa., 1931, p. 10.

tive plan eases the economic burden on both the student and the school.

The technical institutes offering cooperative work programs in 1953–1954 are listed in Table 34. This table indicates the enrollment in technological and "other than" technological curriculums in 1953–1954 and the number of certificates or diplomas awarded in 1952–1953.

Rochester was the first technical institute to inaugurate cooperative courses; it initiated this type of program in the civil, electrical, and mechanical departments in 1912.[7] These courses were discontinued for a time during World War I, when the staff and facilities of the Institute were devoted to training soldiers and rehabilitating disabled veterans. Cooperative courses were reestablished in 1923 and have been operated continuously since that time. At present, three-year cooperative curriculums are offered in the chemical, commerce, electrical, food administration, mechanical, and retailing departments. In the chemical, commerce, electrical, and mechanical departments students alternate at twelve-week intervals; in the food administration and retailing at six-week intervals. All departments now operate on a full-time first-year basis with cooperative work during the last two years. During the school year 1940–1941 a total of 617 students received cooperative work experience,[8] while during the school year 1953–1954 a total of 516 students were on this plan.

[7] *Bulletin of Mechanics Institute* (Rochester, N.Y.), vol. 4, no. 7, p. 14.

[8] In 1940–1941 all three years were on a cooperative basis; hence a considerably larger number of students would be cooperatively employed in any one year than is now the case.

TABLE 34

STATUS OF COOPERATIVE EDUCATION IN TECHNICAL INSTITUTES
1953–1954

| Institution | Enrollment 1953–1954 | | Diplomas to Cooperative Students 1952–1953 | |
|---|---|---|---|---|
| | Technological | Other than Technological | Technological | Other than Technological |
| General Motors Institute | ... | 435 | ... | 179 |
| Broome County Technical Institute | 226 | ... | 62 | ... |
| Erie County Technical Institute | 578 | 67 | 177 | 28 |
| New York City Community College of Applied Arts and Science | ... | 769 | ... | 190 |
| Rochester Institute of Technology | 325 | 191 | 58 | 40 |
| Westchester Community College | 331 | 150 | 100 | ... |
| Ohio Mechanics Institute | 215 | ... | 23 | ... |
| Wyomissing Polytechnic Institute | 135 | ... | 23 | ... |
| Total | 1810 | 1612 | 443 | 437 |

SOURCE: Adapted from H. H. Armsby, *Cooperative Education in the United States*, U.S. Department of Health, Education, and Welfare Bulletin 11, Washington, 1954.

A two-year cooperative power-laundry course was inaugurated at Ohio Mechanics Institute in 1920 and a cooperative industrial engineering curriculum was added later. During the school year 1940–1941, 94 students received cooperative work experience, while during the school year 1948–1949, 153 students were enrolled on this plan.

Wyomissing Polytechnic Institute was chartered as a technical institute in 1933 and has offered a cooperative course since that time.[9] The course consists of five terms of eleven weeks each, and students alternate at four-week intervals. During the school year 1952–1953 enrollment in the cooperative course totaled about 140.

In 1946 the legislature of the State of New York passed a law creating five institutes of applied arts and sciences to be located in Binghamton, Brooklyn, Buffalo, Utica, and White Plains. These institutes were established for a five-year experimental period and are in addition to the six agricultural and technical institutes which have been in operation for many years. At the expiration of the five-year experimental period the institutes were given two periods of extension, each of which was one year in length. The community college law passed in 1952 provides that the state and local communities shall share equally the capital expenditure costs, and the operating costs shall be borne one-third each by the state, the local community, and the students.

These institutions have met a real need in New York

[9] "Technical Institute Profiles: The Wyomissing Polytechnic Institute," *Tech. Educ. News,* August, 1953, p. 5.

and the enrollment has increased rapidly. One aspect of their programs upon which these schools are placing considerable emphasis is the cooperative work plan. Some of these institutes require one six-month work period; others provide for alternating periods of work and study.

During the early years the cooperative curriculums in technical institutes were for the most part offered in engineering fields. The reasons for this are probably similar to those which led to the popularity of cooperative engineering programs in colleges and universities. That is, the technical institutes have been concerned for the most part with training men for supervisory and technical positions in industries requiring relatively large numbers of men with engineering background. This tendency to offer cooperative work in the engineering fields has now shifted somewhat and Table 35 lists the cooperative courses now offered in technical institutes.

### Organizing cooperative work programs

A study of the literature and conversations and correspondence with key people at schools with cooperative programs reveals that several different methods have been employed to initiate cooperative programs. These are:

1. The calling of a general meeting to which interested parties from business and industry are invited to meet with the college representatives.
2. The appointment of advisory committees to suggest steps which should be taken.
3. The use of faculty members and department heads to contact industries for cooperative placement.

TABLE 35

COOPERATIVE EDUCATIONAL PROGRAMS IN TECHNICAL INSTITUTES

1953–54

| Institution | Technological | | | | | | | Other than Technological | | | | | |
|---|---|---|---|---|---|---|---|---|---|---|---|---|---|
| | Automotive | Building Construction | Chemical Technology | Electrical Technology | Industrial Technology | Mechanical Technology | Metallurgical Technology | Business Administration | Dental and Medical Technology | Executive Assisting | Food Service Administration | Hotel Technology | Retailing and Merchandising |
| General Motors Institute | | | | | | | | | | | | | x |
| Broome County Technical Institute | x | | x | x | | x | | | | | | | |
| Erie County Technical Institute | | x | | x | x | x | x | | | | x | | |
| New York City Community College of Applied Arts and Science | | | | | | | | | | x | | x | x |
| Rochester Institute of Technology | | | x | x | | x | | | | | x | | x |
| Westchester Community College | | x | x | x | | x | | x | x | | x | | |
| Ohio Mechanics Institute | | x | x | x | | x | | | | | | | |
| Wyomissing Polytechnic Institute | | | | | x | | | | | | | | |
| Number of institutions offering each curriculum | 1 | 3 | 4 | 5 | 2 | 5 | 1 | 1 | 1 | 1 | 3 | 1 | 3 |

SOURCE: Adapted from H. H. Armsby, *Cooperative Education in the United States*, U.S. Department of Health, Education, and Welfare Bulletin 11, Washington, 1954.

4. The employment of a coordinator to make arrangements for cooperative placement. These methods are interrelated and are often used to supplement each other. Hence it is difficult to evaluate the effectiveness of any one plan, but several generalizations may be made:

1. It is desirable to hold one or more general meetings to which industrialists, labor leaders, and representatives from other institutions with cooperative programs are invited. At this time the basic objectives and purposes of the program may be outlined.

2. The appointment of advisory committees is highly desirable. These committees should not be too large and, in light of the local situation, should include representatives from business, labor, and the school.

3. The use of coordinators is a valuable technique, for these individuals may assume the task of visits to prospective employers, make plans for training circuits, sell the program to industry, students, and faculty. If faculty members are utilized for these tasks, it is essential that they be allowed sufficient time for fulfilling these duties.

### Administering cooperative work programs

The primary objective of a cooperative work program is to provide a series of graded or sequential experiences which will assist the student to integrate his theoretical education in school and his practical work on the job in a meaningful whole. Unless provisions are made for accomplishing this basic purpose, the work periods become little more than intermittent periods of employment. Two principal means have been utilized for administering the program: first, the use of department heads or interested faculty members and, second, the employment of a coordinator or establishment of a central department of coordination. Historically the first method was utilized when the programs were small and had few students enrolled. The second procedures evolved as greater numbers of students were participating in the cooperative plan and it was no longer feasible to consider this a part-time job for a faculty person or department head.

In any cooperative program there are certain administrative duties which must be assumed if the program is to function effectively. The major responsibilities are:

1. Locating jobs.
2. Selecting applicants for jobs.
3. Coordinating school and work experiences.
4. Counseling students about job progress.
5. Counseling students about academic and personal problems.

In the study[10] already referred to, seventeen of the twenty-nine colleges reported that they employed a coordinator or department of coordination to administer the cooperative program. No technical institute employed this method but delegated these responsibilities to department heads or faculty members. The answers from the junior colleges indicated that the problems of administration were about evenly divided between department heads and coordinators.

[10] Smith, *op. cit.*, pp. 87–91.

## Evaluation of techniques of administering cooperative programs

As has already been pointed out, the two principal means of administering cooperative programs are by department heads or interested faculty members and by a coordinator or department of coordination. When the former are used there are several advantages, as follows:

1. The department heads or faculty members are generally well acquainted with students and hence are in a better position to recommend students for cooperative jobs which will be in line with their ability and interest.
2. Because of their more intimate knowledge of students, the department heads or faculty members are in an ideal position to assist them with their personal and vocational problems.

There are also certain disadvantages to the use of this technique:

1. When department heads become burdened with administrative details, they tend to make industrial contacts by telephone, a practice which if carried on over a long period of time results in a loss of good will.
2. Faculty members are likely to view teaching as their primary responsibility and devote only the minimum time required to the duties of administering and coordinating the program.
3. If industries employ cooperative students from several departments, confusion arises as to the proper department head or faculty member to contact.

Two advantages of administration by a coordinator or central department of coordination are significant:

1. Coordinators have generally been selected because they have the type of training, technical background, and personal characteristics deemed desirable for this type of work. Likewise, coordinators view the administration of the cooperative program as their primary duty and hence are likely to devote their full interest and energy to this end.

2. The use of a central office of coordination makes it possible for all contacts with industry to clear through this office.

The major objection which has been raised to the use of a central office of coordination is that the coordinators do not have the close personal contact with students that department heads or faculty members do.

## Coordinating the school and work experiences

One of the primary advantages of cooperative education, as stated by advocates[11,12] of the plan, is that it provides both systematic instruction in principles and practical training in their application. For this reason it is believed that students become better qualified to visualize the relationship between theory and practice. No one will deny that this ability is a highly desirable attainment, but administrators who have been connected with coopera-

[11] Carl S. Ell, "The Social Significance of the Cooperative Plan," *Sch. Soc.*, vol. 41, p. 452, April 6, 1935.

[12] Parke R. Kolbe, "Educational Aspects of the Cooperative Course," *Sch. Soc.*, vol. 51, p. 661, May 25, 1940.

tive programs over a period of years have found that this understanding does not take place automatically for several reasons, of which the following are important:

1. The students during the early years of their cooperative experience may not have sufficient technical background to recognize the practical applications of the theories studied in school.
2. Many of the jobs in which students are placed are repetitive in nature and do not readily lend themselves to broad training purposes.
3. Students are often kept on the same job for so long that they do not have the opportunity to experience more than a very limited number of job operations.

In order to minimize the difficulties which have been mentioned in the foregoing paragraph, numerous techniques have been developed to coordinate the school and work experiences. Following are the ones noted most frequently:

1. Sequential, graded job experiences commensurate with the student's ability to profit by these experiences.
2. Reports by students concerning the experiences which they have had on the work block.
3. Coordination classes in school.
4. Periodic reports from industry concerning student progress.
5. Visits by coordinator to students on the job.

*Graded job experience*

Of the foregoing one of the most important techniques is for the cooperating industries and the school to formu-

TABLE 36

REPRESENTATIVE COOPERATIVE JOB CIRCUIT PLAN

| | Weeks |
|---|---|
| Starting employment in June at the plant: | |
| Orientation (inspection department) | 2 |
| Drafting room | 3 |
| Production department | 3 |
| Industrial engineering | 2 |
| After first year of school: | |
| Machine and pulverizer department | 10 |
| Tube fabricating shop | 10 |
| Steel fabricating shop | 20 |
| Forge (including boiler assembly) | 14 |
| Pattern and foundry | 6 |

late a planned series of experiences which are varied in nature or graded sequentially with respect to the manual skills and understanding of principles required. At the Rochester Institute of Technology considerable progress has been made in securing the cooperation of the employing companies in formulating these graded experiences. Table 36 illustrates the cooperative job circuit plan in effect with one company. The students are to be employed by this company immediately upon graduation from high school and during the first summer are to spend time in the inspection department, drafting room, production department, and industrial engineering as indicated. The students then attend school full time for the first year and during the second and third years of their cooperative course are placed on jobs in various other departments and shops as indicated. These students are being groomed to be supervisors in the various departments and shops and designers of power plant equipment.

It should be understood that the sequence of departments shown in Table 36 is not fixed but may be varied as conditions require. It is expected that all cooperative trainees will spend the summer vacation at the plant. Upon completion of the three-year cooperative course, the trainee continues in training on a full-time basis for approximately 12 months to complete training in the various departments and to become proficient in the operations of at least one department.

*Reports from students*

One of the most frequent methods of coordination is for the educational institutions to require reports from students concerning the experiences which they have had on the work block. On the college level, Northeastern University in Boston has been very specific concerning the types of topics suitable for reports, the form they should take, and their length. Evidence of the importance that this university attaches to these reports is given by the fact that thirteen pages in the handbook given all cooperative students are devoted to a discussion of the methods of presentation and subject matter.

General Motors Institute in Flint, Michigan, also places considerable emphasis on the value of work reports. In the manual of coordination which has been compiled by plant and Institute representatives, twenty-eight pages are devoted to a discussion of reports.

Although some of the technical institutes utilize cooperative reports as a method of coordination, none of them place as much emphasis upon this technique as Northeastern University and General Motors Institute.

*Periodic reports from industry*

Some institutions obtain periodic reports from cooperating firms concerning the performance of cooperative students. While there are difficulties involved in obtaining these reports or ratings, there are certain definite advantages of this method to the student, the school and the industries:

1. It forces supervisors to view the students working under them as individuals with varying aptitudes, abilities, and interests.
2. It enables the schools to identify those students who are having difficulty in making adjustments to the job and their fellow workers.
3. Assuming that institutions utilize these reports for counseling purposes, it provides the student with an indication as to how adequately he is meeting the requirements of the job.

*Visits by coordinators to students on the job*

The technique of having coordinators visit students on the job is one which has been utilized with considerable variation in emphasis at the several levels of education. Colleges and universities employ this method only occasionally. Rochester is the only technical institute to utilize this technique, and it is used principally by the retailing department coordinator.

## Evaluation of the techniques of coordination

It would be very desirable and satisfying if it were possible to make an evaluation of the techniques of coordination which would permit statistical treatment. It would be interesting and probably of help to educators if it were possible to indicate the degree or rate that students developed in the ability to apply principles, in their over-all mental growth or maturation, and in the enthusiasm with which they attacked their schoolwork, if one or another or a combination of coordination methods were employed. Unfortunately, no studies are available in this area, but it is believed that the following generalizations are justified:

1. The cooperative placement which appears to hold the greatest value to the student, the school, and the employer is one in which the latter provides a series of sequential, graded job experiences related to the student's major course. Without exception, leaders in the field of cooperative education state that it would be highly desirable if all industries would outline and adhere to such a training program. The fact that industries have not gone as far in this direction as seems desirable does not mean necessarily that there is an unwillingness to cooperate, but owing to the needs for meeting production schedules and the problems involved in convincing all parties concerned of the potential values, it is difficult to initiate and carry out such a program.
2. The use of reports submitted by students is a coordination technique which has considerable potential value.

In this area considerable progress has been made, and some of the reports required by Antioch, Cincinnati, Northeastern, and Northwestern give evidence of much study, planning, and understanding on the part of the student.

3. The reports which educational institutions obtain from industry on cooperative students may be of considerable assistance in counseling. It is probable that these reports are of greatest value when the coordinator has done a careful job of explaining to the supervisor in industry the purpose and function of these reports. Another generalization which may also be made is that the reports should not be required too frequently.

4. The other techniques of coordination, such as coordination classes, personal interviews with students following the work block, and visits to students on the job, have their place but appear to vary considerably in their effectiveness.

CHAPTER 13

# Administration

The administration of any educational institution, be it technical institute, college, university, or secondary school, is the performance of certain executive duties in order that the objectives of the institution may be achieved. Areas of administrative concern in a technical institute may include basic source of control, organizational structure, finances, business administration, plant, the instructional program, student personnel administration, public relations, and evaluation. While administration consists essentially of making policies and decisions, the test of its efficiency lies in the extent to which the educational aims, goals or objectives are reached.

In the foregoing chapters the various activities and functions of technical institutes have been described. It has been implied that some guiding force or person was responsible for initiating and supervising these functions. The purpose of this chapter is to describe the administrative patterns and problems of technical institutes and to outline the principal responsibilities of a technical institute administration.

## General control

Every technical institute has its origin in some objective, conceived at least in general terms by some individual, group, or legislative body. The initiating force then determines the basic plan of financing.

Institutions whose curriculums are primarily of the technical institute type have three principal means of support:

1. Public support, by states or municipalities.
2. Private endowment and support, with nonprofit operation.
3. Private support (proprietary institutions) with operation for a profit.

The source of financial support is a key factor in determining the composition of the policy-making body.

"The typical American plan for the control of an institution of higher education provides for a board in which final authority is lodged."[1] This board of trustees or board of directors is typically composed of laymen. By charter or articles of incorporation, the board becomes legally responsible as the ultimate source of control for the institution.

The board's concern with long-range policies calls for terms of office which will be long enough to permit the member to become thoroughly familiar with the institute. (A term of six years or longer has been suggested.[2]) It is

[1] John Dale Russell and Floyd W. Reeves, *The Evaluation of Higher Institutions,* University of Chicago Press, Chicago, 1936, p. 17.

[2] *Revised Manual of Accrediting,* North Central Association of Colleges and Secondary Schools, 1941, p. 17.

also suggested that terms expire at different times, as in the United States Senate. The principles guiding the selection of board members will be determined by the objectives of the institution. Board members of publicly supported institutes are chosen to represent the public interest. In the case of privately endowed institutes, board members are usually chosen to represent the industrial, business, and community interests served by the institute and they are often important donors. Many proprietary institutes function like other businesses, with the principal owner exercising administrative direction as well as financial control.

A board of control is usually conceived as a body which will determine policy but which will not directly administer its own policies. Since the board is composed of laymen, its main concern is with broad goals, and the details of the methods utilized in reaching them are more logically left to the professional educators and specialists employed by the board. The basic supervisory function of the board of control is typically delegated to the chief executive officer, such as the president or principal. To the president, the board delegates the responsibility of making all operational decisions consistent with adopted policy and of pointing out to the board the shifts in policy needed because of changing conditions.[3] The maintenance of clear-cut lines of authority requires that all other employees should be subordinate to the executive officer.

[3] Walter R. Goetsch, "Organization of the University for Administration and Development," *Current Trends in Higher Education, 1948,* National Education Association, Washington, 1948, p. 162.

An important function of a board of control is discharged when it employs a chief executive officer and delegates to him appropriate responsibilities and authority. However, there are additional matters so basic to the welfare of the institute that they cannot be delegated entirely. These include obtaining and investing funds and determining general policies. Bogue has described the functions of a board of control in more detail.[4]

## Organizational structure

Goetsch has pointed out that there are four rather obvious divisions of administrative structure in institutions of higher education.[5] "(*a*) academic administration, (*b*) student personnel administration, (*c*) business administration, and (*d*) administration of field services and pub-

[4] "(1) To determine general policies for organization, administration, and operation. . . . (2) To act as court of final appeal in all matters which may properly be referred to it. (3) To approve the budget and authorize changes within the limits of the budget and authorize changes within the span of the fiscal year. (4) To assume responsibility for securing funds for . . . proper operation. (5) To employ the chief executive, unless otherwise specified, and delegate to him powers and responsibilities under a written contract. (6) To elect major staff members and teaching personnel on recommendation of the chief executive, unless otherwise specified. In this respect the chief executive should have just as free a hand as possible in the selection of his staff. . . . (7) To authorize and execute contracts for major capital improvements. (8) To authorize investment and provide protection for all funds given in trust. . . . (9) To authorize by formal vote the granting of degrees of graduation of candidates certified by the faculty, registrar, and chief executive." Jesse P. Bogue, *The Community College,* McGraw-Hill Book Company, Inc., New York, 1950, pp. 282–3.

[5] Goetsch, *op. cit.,* p. 161.

lic relations." In the smaller technical institutes it is customary for the department or unit heads to report directly to the president. In the larger institutes it is more common for the departments or units to be grouped in various ways for administrative efficiency. The following chart illustrates one pattern which has been utilized. In such an organization the president or principal has responsibility for employing and supervising department heads, who, in turn, supervise the instructional staff. It is recommended that department heads at least share the responsibility for selecting their faculty members.[6]

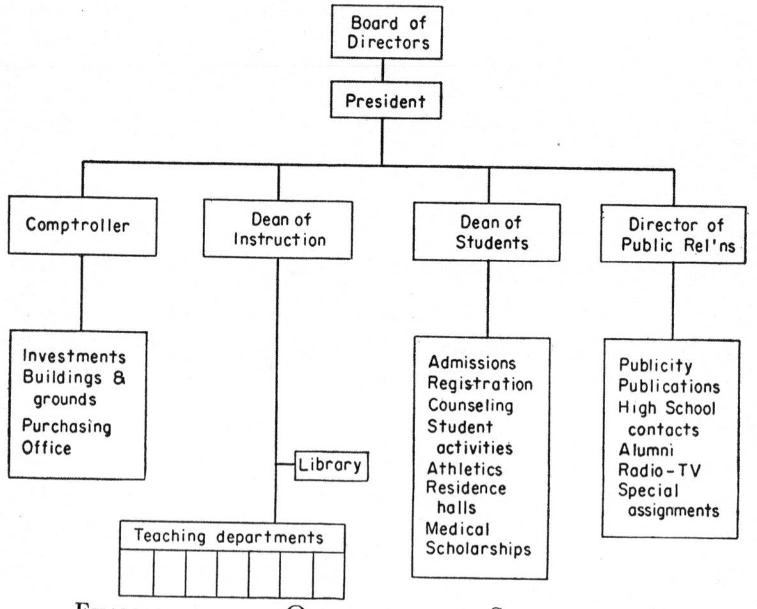


EXAMPLE OF THE ORGANIZATIONAL STRUCTURE OF A TECHNICAL INSTITUTE

[6] Cf. *Revised Manual of Accrediting, op. cit.*, pp. vii, 5.

In the larger institutes a line organization may have additional echelons, or it may be supplemented with staff personnel, like counselors, business office workers, and librarians, who serve the entire institution and who report to the president or to some other line executive. A line and staff type of organization may also be supplemented by various committees for the determination of general policy, for awarding scholarships, for curriculum construction, or for other purposes.

In considering administrative structure, it is particularly important to bear in mind that administration exists only to serve the institute's objectives and that the best pattern is that which fits the particular needs of the institute.

## Finances

Once a technical institute president has been appointed, financial policy is one of his most critical responsibilities, subject to the advice and approval of his board of control or advisory groups he may consult. In the case of a public institution, the president must prepare a budget, and it is his responsibility to see that the necessary funds are obtained from his legislative body. In the case of private institutions the budgetary problems are similar, but the sources of funds are different and the techniques may differ. The financing of a proprietary institute has much in common with the management of any other profit-making business.

Most endowed institutes obtain a fairly high percentage of their operating funds from tuition. Return from invested endowment funds is another vital source of income which is particularly important in determining the financial soundness and stability of the institute. Certain institutes may have additional special sources of funds, for example, Alliance Technical Institute, which is sponsored by the Polish National Alliance.

Up until the present time, the principal source of endowment funds has been private individuals who have both substantial wealth and a philanthropic interest in the institute type of education. This is still an important source, but the number of private fortunes is decreasing. Although the present tax structure tends to encourage philanthropies by wealthy individuals, it limits the development of new fortunes.

Colleges and universities, faced with the same problem, have given considerable attention to such fund-raising techniques as canvassing alumni and banding together into regional associations for fund-raising purposes. For further information about fund-raising, reference may be made to the sources listed below.[7-9]

There are indications that business and industrial companies will provide one of the most productive sources of funds for technical institutes in the future. One reason is that large companies, if profitable, have substantial funds available. The technical institute type of curriculum is

[7] Frank E. Andrews, *Attitudes toward Giving,* Russell Sage Foundation, New York, 1953.

[8] Charles W. Gamble, *How to Raise Money,* Association Press, New York, 1942.

[9] Ernest V. Hollis, *Philanthropic Foundations and Higher Education,* Columbia University Press, New York, 1938.

particularly important to industry, and the tax structure permits corporations to make gifts of this type without excessive sacrifice. The Rochester Institute of Technology has made outstanding strides in this field. At present its operating budget is made up approximately as follows: one-half from tuition, one-quarter from return on endowment, and one-quarter from annual grants by business and industrial firms.

Institutes with all types of financial support can benefit from gifts of equipment from interested manufacturers. It is often in the financial interest of a manufacturer to give or lend equipment and machinery for instructional purposes. Technical institute students are potential executives, and their familiarity with a piece of machinery may influence them to purchase that type when they reach executive positions. In other instances, it may be worth while for a company to lend to the institute equipment which is used by that firm, so that students who have laboratory practice on these machines will be better trained when they begin employment. From the standpoint of the institute, a safeguard to keep in view is that the acceptance of gifts and loans of equipment should be fair to all manufacturers and prospective employers of graduates.

### Business administration

The funds accumulated by a technical institute serve the institution's objectives only to the extent that they are managed efficiently. Specialized business management services are required (1) to care for administrative details so as to permit academic officers and faculty members to devote their time primarily to instructional activities and (2) to conserve financial resources for the maximum support of the institution's educational services.[10] The business administration functions of a technical institute may include financial accounting, budgeting, purchasing, payroll, and other activities commonly found in most businesses. In addition, an institute may have special problems in collecting tuition and other fees, supervising the finances of student activities, and placing special insurance coverage.

Many of the relevant principles and problems of institute business administration are of such general application in business management that they do not warrant special attention in this chapter. However, it should be mentioned that the budget has been widely recognized as the logical method for controlling the finances of a technical institute to reconcile expenditures with income. Russell and Reeves[11] suggest that the following items be included in a budget:

1. Proposed budget last completed year.
2. Actual results last fiscal year.
3. Budget for current year.
4. Present estimate of outcome for current year.
5. Proposed budget for next year.
6. Increases or decreases from last year.

Typical procedure calls for departments to submit budget requests and for the chief administrative officer

[10] Russell and Reeves, *op. cit.*, p. 77.
[11] *Ibid.*, p. 94.

to exercise final authority in reconciling these requests with expected income. It is important for the time schedule to be arranged so that these steps can be completed in plenty of time for action by the ultimate source of control, such as a legislative body or board of trustees.

Financing student activities presents many problems because of the annual turnover of student officers, the diversity of activities, and the separation of student funds from institutional funds. In many instances, an institute's business office will collect separate fees for student activities. In other instances, such as athletic events and dramatics, fees may be collected at the gate. For efficient management of their funds, student organizations are almost certain to need professional guidance, the most available source of which is the business office. Budgeting, accounting, and auditing methods may be devised to meet the particular needs. In connection with the training of student officers, it may be possible for the business office to cooperate with student personnel officers.

## Plant

The objectives and program of an institute determine the type of plant required. Most technical institutes require considerable floor space for shops and laboratories. The specificity of these needs makes it particularly important to design buildings "from the inside out." In other words, the equipment needed may have an important bearing on the type of building which will house it. If a separate building is used primarily for classroom purposes, there may be more flexibility in its exterior design, although it will still be important to have the interior arranged in rooms of suitable size, with seating appropriate for the type of instruction planned. Other considerations in a classroom building may be rooms for film projection and private offices for administrators and student personnel workers.

Many institutes, particularly at the time of their founding, have made effective use of buildings designed for other purposes. Former public schools, private homes, office buildings, factory buildings, and warehouses have been utilized. At least one institute is utilizing quonset-type buildings, which provide very suitable interiors although the esthetic appeal of the exterior is limited.

In higher institutions generally, a campus type of plant has come to be traditional. This type has several advantages:

1. It can utilize the esthetic properties of landscaping.
2. Each building can be designed for a specific purpose.
3. A campus of sufficient size offers opportunities for convenient expansion through the construction of new buildings.
4. A campus can create a sense of unity or group feeling on the part of the students.

In most nonurban institutes a campus has developed logically, more or less along the lines established by colleges and universities. Many technical institutes, however, derive their principal source of strength from their close ties with the businesses and industries in a specific metropolitan area. An urban location has more influences toward a plant which consists of a small number of buildings, placed in close proximity. The cost of land is one of these influences. Accessibility to the whole commuting area may be important for both day students and adult evening students. It should be borne in mind, however, that location on a streetcar or bus line may cease to be important if most students drive their own cars and require parking space. One outstanding advantage of a plant consisting of one or a few buildings is that maintenance costs are significantly less than they would be for equal space on a campus.

In connection with planning a technical institute plant, the following questions are among those which must be answered:

1. What facilities and equipment does the curriculum require?
2. What buildings are already available?
3. What is the prospective enrollment at present; in five years; in ten years; in twenty years?
4. What needs must be met in respect to extracurricular activities of students?
5. What opportunities for expansion does the site provide?
6. How do transportation facilities meet the needs of students and prospective students?
7. How do the maintenance costs of the proposed plant compare with those of alternative sites?
8. What esthetic factors are relevant?
9. What dormitory facilities are needed?

### Administering the instructional program

A primary factor in determining the effectiveness of a technical institute program is what takes place in the individual classroom.

Some of the problems of recruiting and training faculty have been discussed in Chapter 4. From the administrative standpoint, however, there are some other important considerations which should be mentioned.

Financial considerations enter very significantly into the problem of faculty–student ratio. Operation is more economical if it is possible to conduct instruction in large classes. Research indicates that they are feasible in certain subjects where the lecture method is used. However, relatively small classes are required for genuine class discussions and for individual attention in a shop or laboratory. In one institution, laboratory rooms were deliberately made small in a new building so that there would be no temptation to increase class size beyond a certain point. On the other hand, it should be borne in mind that small classes are not necessarily better in every situation. It is important for an administrator to review the institutional objectives and to evaluate carefully the extent to which they may be attained by the various approaches which are available.

Few technical institute instructors seek their positions primarily because of the salary. Income opportunities, however, have an important effect on the type of individual who may be recruited. To hire a person with sound technical competence, an institute usually must pay a salary which does not compare too unfavorably with what the individual could earn in industry. However, the interest of some individuals in technical institute teaching is such that industrial wages would seldom need to be exceeded. Good general education instructors usually may be recruited only if salaries are comparable with those offered by other educational institutions.

A technical institute can offer faculty members advantages in pleasant working conditions, advancement, stability of employment, and provision for retirement. These advantages, however, do not come automatically. They exist only if the administration makes suitable provisions and carries out appropriate policies.

### Student personnel administration

The administrative attitude toward students and student life is a key factor which affects recruitment, student morale, alumni relationships, and many other aspects of a technical institute's program. Some of the administrative attitudes which exist in technical institutes, consciously or unconsciously, are listed below:

1. The high school attitude prevails, with students being told what to do and generally treated as too immature to carry independent responsibility.
2. Students are treated as adults and left mainly on their own.
3. A paternalistic attitude is the basis of faculty-planned activities designed to be of value to students.
4. Attention is concentrated on the curriculum and other aspects of student life are ignored.

5. Student activities are tolerated as a necessary evil but are not encouraged or exploited for the attainment of educational objectives.

6. Opportunities are provided for student leadership and responsibility in developing out-of-class activities which will meet their needs and foster their development.

Philosophical justification can be found for a variety of administrative policies toward students. It is not the purpose of this chapter to discuss these philosophies at length. From the administrative viewpoint, however, the following principles apply:

1. Student activities and regulations affecting students are important enough to deserve careful study.

2. The development of a consistent, long-range policy will eliminate a feeling of moving from crisis to crisis.

3. A policy will be most effectively carried out if administrative responsibilities are made clear to all concerned.

4. Administration at any level is most effective if authority is commensurate with responsibility.

In connection with the foregoing points, written constitutions for student organizations have been found effective in clarifying responsibility. It is implicit in most institutes that the seat of authority is in the board of control and that this authority is delegated to the administration. These facts are not always understood by students, however, and if a particular area of responsibility is delegated to students, a written document and frank discussions of the subject can eliminate sources of conflict.

## Public relations

It is not the function of this section to include a thorough discussion of institutional public relations.[12] Rather, an attempt will be made to highlight some of the public relations factors which are of special significance for a technical institute.

The source of financial support may be a key factor in determining the area in which relationships outside of the institute count the most. Direct or indirect contacts with a legislative body may be particularly important for institutes having public support, whereas a private institution may be more concerned with the groups or individuals most interested in its program.

All technical institutes need satisfactory relationships with the industries which they serve. This may be important for curriculum planning, for placement of graduates, for gifts and loans of equipment, and for other financial support. In this connection, advisory committees are important, not only for their specific advisory functions, but also as a medium for continuing communication and good will.

High schools in the institute's recruiting area are particularly important in the institute's public relations program. It is important not only to work toward the development of a favorable attitude toward the institute but also to bring about a clear understanding of the insti-

[12] For a more comprehensive discussion see W. Emerson Reck, *College Publicity Manual,* Harper & Brothers, New York, 1948.

tute's program, which may be unfamiliar to many high school teachers and students.

In connection with any public relations activity it is important to remember that the feelings of students, alumni, and faculty toward the institute will have a more significant effect than publicity material prepared by a professional public relations expert. Many individuals connected with an institute are constantly in contact with various sections of the public, and public relations will be most effective if their efforts are coordinated.

## Evaluation

The chief administrator has a responsibility to evaluate all aspects of the institute's program. Some of the areas of evaluation are instruction, plant and equipment, financing, public relations, student personnel activities, and curriculum content.

Executive decisions in any enterprise are sound only to the extent that they are based on accurate data. In the educational field the most important source of data lies in measures of the extent to which the objectives of the institution are being attained.

One of the key aspects of educational evaluation is student achievement in the curriculum. Tyler has outlined in detail the steps involved in this type of evaluation, and the most important of these are as follows:[13]

1. Formulation of the objectives of each course or curriculum and definition of these in terms of the changes in

[13] Adapted from Ralph W. Tyler, "Measuring Individual Accomplishments," *Personnel J.*, vol. 12, p. 215.

knowledge, information, skills, attitudes, or appreciations desired in students.

2. Collection of situations which give students opportunity to demonstrate the extent to which they have achieved each objective.

3. Organization of these situations into tests, check lists of observation, etc., and the administration of these to students.

4. Scoring of the tests, check lists, and other devices used.

5. Critical review of entire procedure of evaluation in terms of relevance to the objectives, reliability, validity, and practicability of use.

In most institutes each instructor constructs his own tests or check lists according to his best judgment. These may or may not be adequate and reliable measures of the content that it is desired to measure. Test construction is a complicated field, in which a classroom instructor without special training cannot be expected to be expert.

When an institution has objectives whose attainment cannot be measured with paper-and-pencil tests of subject matter, the problem becomes more acute. How should an institute measure the development of initiative and self-reliance on the part of the student? How can one determine the extent to which a student has developed a constructive attitude toward work? If the institute has objectives of this kind, it is important to measure their achievement.

To fulfill his obligations in this type of evaluation, an administrator may have several courses open to him. He may encourage one or more faculty members to obtain suitable training in evaluation, he may employ a specialist, or he may engage a part-time consultant to assist his faculty from time to time with this and other problems.

The use of educational consultants has been a key factor in evaluation and administration at the Rochester Institute of Technology since 1928. Between their visits the Coordinator of Educational Research works cooperatively with the faculty in determining the problems to be presented to the consultants and the steps to be taken to work toward the solution of problems already identified. In an earlier article Ellingson and Jarvie outline the philosophy underlying this program:[14]

> Throughout the program it is evident that the consultants and the chairman of the Research Committee are considered as counselors to the staff . . . that the real steps toward the solution of problems and improvement of program must be taken by the persons most vitally concerned; that consultants as counselors must to a large extent be stimulators of teacher development; and that they must aid teachers in visualizing problems more clearly and provide aid in exploring possible patterns of attack.

In the case of a technical institute, where attainment of occupational preparation is a key objective, information about the employment of graduates is an essential element in evaluation. Chapter 5 illustrates both the facts

[14] Mark Ellingson and Lawrence L. Jarvie, "The Role of Consultants in Education," *J. Higher Educ.*, vol. 12, p. 83, February, 1941.

and techniques that technical institutes have evolved in connection with follow-up of graduates.

Evaluation of the effectiveness of the instructional staff involves a look at the other side of some of the same problems that relate to student achievement. Systematic procedures may be utilized to measure the effectiveness of instructors. Use of the same test in class sections taught by different instructors is one method. Another is questioning students through a questionnaire or interviews about the instructors' methods and effectiveness.[15] Clues may also be obtained through meetings between the department head and the instructor. Many administrators feel that effectiveness within the classroom is only one of several important qualifications of an instructor. Other factors may include effectiveness in committee and curriculum assignments, public relations contacts, and student personnel activities.

One aspect of evaluation includes the techniques which may be utilized to obtain relevant facts. Another aspect is the way these facts are interpreted or judged. The determination of "good" or "bad" can be made only in terms of some set of values. In the final analysis these values are based on philosophy rather than on objective facts, and there is room for legitimate differences of opinion. Whatever an institute's philosophy of administration may be, it will be implemented most effectively if it is consciously understood, so that measures can be planned to achieve the desired goals.

[15] A copy of such a questionnaire is included in Appendix 8.

## General principles

Among technical institutes there is considerable variety in objectives, financial resources, community influences, and other factors which lead very logically to corresponding variety in administrative patterns and practices.

However, there are a number of general principles of administration which apply to all technical institutes.[16] The most important of these are as follows:

1. The objectives of the institute and its various activities are most likely to be achieved if they are clearly formulated and understood.

2. Each activity of the institution exists primarily for the purpose of achieving the basic objectives. This includes not only instruction but also student personnel services, public relations, business management, and plant maintenance.

3. Policies are likely to be carried out more effectively and enthusiastically if the persons concerned participate in the formulation of those policies.

4. Sound decisions require accurate information. Obtaining it requires effective techniques of evaluation and fact-gathering.

5. At each echelon of administration the policy-makers need effective channels of communication *from* subordinates as well as methods of communicating policies *to* sub-

[16] Cf. Enock C. Dyrness, "Institutional Organization and Administration," *Current Trends in Higher Education, 1949,* National Education Association, Washington, 1949, p. 152.

ordinates and supervising the carrying out of those policies.

6. Administration is effective only to the extent that authority is commensurate with responsibility.

7. Effective coordination of various individuals and departments requires a clear understanding of the respective responsibilities and authority of the participants.

8. Orderly administration requires that subordinates be selected and trained systematically to fill vacancies in administrative posts.

9. Most people are able to adapt to progress and change gradually but not suddenly. This suggests that smooth administration is evolutionary rather than revolutionary.

CHAPTER 14

# The Technical Institute and the Future

Part One of this volume has described existing technical institutes in respect to general characteristics, curriculums, course content, and placement of graduates. Part Two has outlined the problems and principles involved in initiating, developing, and administering technical institute programs. These chapters have brought out the considerable amount of evolution and development through which technical institutes have passed. It has been made equally clear that technical institutes are still in a dynamic state and are currently undergoing relatively rapid change. As these institutions work toward the fulfillment of their promise, there are suggestions that the direction of their change will take some of the following pathways:

1. Technical institutes may be expected to enroll larger numbers of students. Population studies show that the number of people of college age will increase greatly in the next decade or two. It may be expected that a reasonable proportion of them will attend technical institutes. In addition to the absolute growth in population, there

are additional factors which suggest that technical institutes will enroll a larger *percentage* of youth. One of these factors is the need of industry for technicians. Industry's needs are estimated to be between three and five technicians for every engineer, but enrollment in technical institutes and engineering colleges is in inverse ratio, or approximately three engineering students for every technical institute student. Technical institutes are increasing their efforts and their effectiveness in bringing their message to the attention of youth.

2. Technical institutes are clarifying their position in the educational scene. At one period in their development technical institutes offered courses for non–high school graduates which were basically trade-level courses of the type now common in technical and industrial high schools. At the other end of the scale, some technical institutes have offered programs which came close to engineering curriculums in extent and difficulty. There is now an increasing tendency to standardize on post–high school courses of one to three years in length which clearly are neither trade courses nor engineering courses. As technical institutes themselves have clarified their position, the public likewise is beginning to have a clearer concept of the technical institute's unique role in education. However, as the technical institute crystallizes its place in education, there is a danger that it may become stylized and lose the unique flexibility which has been one of its strengths.

3. There is increasing public support for the technical institute type of education. Within the past decade public-supported institutes have been founded in Connecticut,

Georgia, Indiana, New Hampshire, New York, Oklahoma, Oregon, and Pennsylvania.

4. The education of adults is being accepted more and more as a responsibility of technical institutes. The same faculty and facilities which are designed for the education of young men and women as technicians are equally appropriate for offering courses which will help adults upgrade themselves in industry. Institutes are increasingly taking steps to meet this type of demand on the part of both industry and adult students.

5. Closer integration with industry is being sought by technical institutes. There has always been a close relationship with industry because the primary goal of institutes has been the preparation of graduates for a specific job or cluster of jobs. More extensive use of the cooperative plan offers one means of achieving closer coordination with industry. Institutes are making more effective use of cooperative arrangements now in existence, through clear-cut job circuits and supervisory techniques. There has also been a tendency for a particular industrial firm to work out with a technical institute a special program for trainees.

6. The amount and quality of general education in technical institutes is increasing. Our society has become increasingly aware of the need of all persons for knowledge and skills which make possible effective and satisfying participation not only in work but also in leisure pursuits and in civic and social activities. This educational need is being met to an increasing extent by technical institutes.

Technical institutes have accomplished much in the past, in preparing young people for useful and satisfying careers and in supplying industry with competent employees. An unusual amount of pioneering has been required on the part of technical institutes to carve out their place in education.

The steps that remain to be taken make it clear that continued pioneering will be required if technical institutes fulfill their promise of providing more complete and effective service in an important area of education.

## Appendix 1. Technical institute programs accredited by the Engineers' Council for Professional Development[1]

Since there has not been developed any generally accepted terminology that permits full identification of a curriculum of technical institute type by its title alone, a brief statement of the aims and scope of each curriculum is given in the listing that follows. Accreditation denotes that the curriculum has been examined and that it has been found satisfactory for the stated purpose it is designed to serve. Accreditation does not necessarily imply that a curriculum is essentially equivalent in content or purpose to other curriculums bearing the same or similar titles.

Academy of Aeronautics
(LaGuardia Field, New York)
Aircraft Design and Construction
A resident full-time program of instruction requiring five terms during a period of two and one-half years or a part-time evening program requiring five terms during a period of four and one-half years and leading to the award of a certificate of graduation upon successful completion.
Aircraft Maintenance
Terms II, III, and IV of a resident full-time program of instruction requiring three terms during a period of one and one-half years or a part-time evening program requiring three terms

[1] The list of accredited institutes and descriptions of curriculums is reprinted with permission from Engineers' Council for Professional Development, *Technical Institute Programs in the United States, 1954,* New York, 1954, pp. 5–13.

during a period of three years and leading to the award of a certificate of graduation upon successful completion.

Aircraft Technology

A resident full-time program of instruction requiring six terms during a period of two and three-quarter years or a part-time evening program requiring six terms during a period of five years and leading to the award of a certificate of graduation upon successful completion.

**The Aeronautical University**
(Chicago)

Aeronautical Engineering Drafting

A resident full-time program of instruction requiring two and one-half semesters and leading to the award of a diploma upon successful completion.

Aeronautical Engineering Technology

A resident full-time program of instruction requiring six terms during a period of two years and leading to the award of an associate degree upon successful completion.

**Capitol Radio Engineering Institute**
(Washington)

Resident Course in Practical Radio and Television Engineering

A resident full-time program of instruction requiring a minimum time equivalent to two and one-half semesters. Under a system of individual progress the average time required to complete the work is equivalent to five semesters. The program leads to the award of an Associate in Applied Science degree.

Correspondence Course in Practical Radio and Television Engineering

A program of home-study courses requiring the equivalent of two and one-half to five semesters to complete and leading to the award of a diploma upon successful completion determined by examination.

**Central Technical Institute, Inc.** [Formerly Central Radio and Television Schools]
(Kansas City, Missouri)

Basic Radio-Television

A resident full-time program of instruction requiring the equivalent of four semesters and leading to the award of a diploma upon successful completion.

Electronics, Radio, and Television Technology

A resident full-time program of instruction requiring the equivalent of six semesters and leading to the award of an Associate degree upon successful completion.

Correspondence Course in Master Radio, Television, Electronics Training

A program of home-study courses requiring the equivalent of four semesters plus eight weeks of resident instruction and leading to the award of a diploma upon successful completion determined by examination.

**Cogswell Polytechnical College**
(San Francisco)

Machine Design

A resident full-time program of instruction requiring four semesters during a period of two years and leading to the award of a diploma of graduation upon successful completion.

Structural Design

A resident full-time program of instruction requiring four semesters during a period of two years and leading to the award of a diploma of graduation upon successful completion.

**Franklin Technical Institute**
(Boston)

Industrial Chemistry

A resident full-time program of instruction requiring four semesters and leading to the award of a certificate upon successful completion.

Industrial Electricity

A resident full-time program of instruction requiring four semesters and leading to the award of a certificate upon successful completion.

Mechanical and Machine Design

A resident full-time program of instruction requiring four semesters and leading to the award of a certificate upon successful completion.

Structural Design and Architectural Drafting

A resident full-time program of instruction requiring four semesters and leading to the award of a certificate upon successful completion.

**Franklin University—Technical Institute**

(Columbus, Ohio)

Radio-Television

A resident full-time program of instruction requiring three terms during a period of one year and leading to the award of a certificate upon successful completion.

**University of Houston—College of Technology**

(Houston, Texas)

Air-Conditioning and Refrigeration Technician

A resident full-time program of instruction requiring four semesters and leading to the award of a Certificate of Achievement or an Associate in Science diploma.

Diesel Technician

A resident full-time program of instruction requiring four semesters and leading to the award of a Certificate of Achievement or an Associate in Science diploma.

Industrial Electricity

A resident full-time program of instruction requiring four semesters and leading to the award of a Certificate of Achievement or an Associate in Science diploma.

Stationary Engineering Technology

A resident full-time program of instruction requiring four semesters and leading to the award of a Certificate of Achievement or an Associate in Science diploma.

Technical Radio and Electronics

A resident full-time program of instruction requiring five semesters and leading to the award of a Certificate of Achievement or an Associate in Science diploma.

**Lain Drafting College**
(Indianapolis, Indiana)

Architectural Drafting

A resident full-time program of instruction requiring eight terms during a period of two years and leading to the award of a diploma upon successful completion.

Industrial Engineering Technology

A resident full-time program of instruction requiring eight terms during a period of two years and leading to the award of a diploma upon successful completion.

Tool and Gage Design

A resident full-time program of instruction requiring nine terms during a period of two years and leading to the award of a diploma upon successful completion.

**Milwaukee School of Engineering**
(Milwaukee, Wisconsin)

Electrotechnician

A resident full-time program of instruction requiring four terms during a period of one year and leading to the award of a certificate upon successful completion.

Electronics Technician

A resident full-time program of instruction requiring four terms during a period of one year and leading to the award of a certificate upon successful completion.

Radio Television Technician

A resident full-time program of instruction requiring six terms during a period of one and one-half years and leading to the award of a certificate upon successful completion.

Refrigeration, Heating, and Air-Conditioning Technician

Terms 5, 6, 7, and 8 of a resident full-time program of instruction requiring four terms during a period of one year and leading to the award of a certificate upon successful completion.

Welding Technician

A resident full-time program of instruction requiring four terms during a period of one year and leading to the award of a certificate upon successful completion.

New York State Agricultural and Technical Institute
(Alfred, New York)

Diesel Technology

A resident full-time program of instruction requiring six terms during a period of two years and leading to the award of an Associate in Applied Science degree.

Electrical Technology, with options in Electric Power and in Electric Communications.

A resident full-time program of instruction requiring six terms during a period of two years and leading to the award of an Associate in Applied Science degree.

Heating and Air-Conditioning

A resident full-time program of instruction requiring six terms during a period of two years and leading to the award of an Associate in Applied Science degree.

Mechanical Technology

A resident full-time program of instruction requiring six terms during a period of two years and leading to the award of an Associate in Applied Science degree.

New York State Agricultural and Technical Institute
(Canton, New York)

Electrical Technology

A resident full-time program of instruction requiring four semesters and leading to the award of an Associate in Applied Science degree or a certificate of attendance depending upon individual attainment.

Mechanical Technology—Drafting and Design

A resident full-time program of instruction requiring four semesters and leading to the award of an Associate in Applied Science degree or a certificate of attendance depending upon individual attainment.

Mechanical Technology—Heating, Refrigeration, and Air Conditioning

A resident full-time program of instruction requiring four semesters and leading to the award of an Associate in Applied Science degree or a certificate of attendance depending upon individual attainment.

**Northrop Aeronautical Institute**
(Inglewood, California)

Aeronautical Engineering Technology

A resident full-time program of instruction requiring six terms during a period of two years and leading to the award of a diploma upon successful completion.

**Ohio Mechanics Institute**
(Cincinnati, Ohio)

Construction Technology

A resident full-time cooperative program of instruction requiring four semesters at the institute and forty-seven weeks of industrial cooperative training and leading to the award of an Associate of Science degree upon successful completion.

Electrical Engineering Technology

A resident full-time cooperative program of instruction requiring four semesters at the institute and forty-seven weeks of industrial cooperative training and leading to the award of an Associate of Science degree upon successful completion.

Mechanical Engineering Technology

A resident full-time cooperative program of instruction requiring four semesters at the institute and forty-seven weeks of industrial cooperative training and leading to the award of an Associate of Science degree upon successful completion.

**Oklahoma A. and M. College—School of Technical Training**
(Stillwater, Oklahoma)

Air Conditioning and Refrigeration

A resident full-time program of instruction requiring four semesters and leading to the award of a technician's certificate upon successful completion.

Building Construction

A resident full-time program of instruction requiring four semesters and leading to the award of a technician's certificate upon successful completion.

Drafting and Design

A resident full-time program of instruction requiring four semesters and leading to the award of a technician's certificate upon successful completion.

Diesel and Stationary Engines

A resident full-time program of instruction requiring four semesters and leading to the award of a technician's certificate upon successful completion.

Electrical Technology

A resident full-time program of instruction requiring four semesters and leading to the award of a technician's certificate upon successful completion.

Fire Protection

A resident full-time program of instruction requiring four semesters and leading to the award of a technician's certificate upon successful completion.

Radio and Electronics

A resident full-time program of instruction requiring four semesters and leading to the award of a technician's certificate upon successful completion.

Oregon Technical Institute
(Oretech, Oregon)

Engineering Design Technology

A resident full-time program of instruction requiring six terms during a period of two years and leading to the award of a diploma upon successful completion.

Surveying Technology

A resident full-time program of instruction requiring six terms during a period of two years and leading to the award of a diploma upon successful completion.

**Pennsylvania State University Technical Institutes**
(University Park, Pennsylvania)

Building Construction

An extension center full-time or part-time evening program of instruction requiring two semesters or the equivalent in part-time work and leading to the award of an extension diploma upon successful completion.

Industrial Electricity

An extension center full-time or part-time evening program of instruction requiring two semesters or the equivalent in part-time work and leading to the award of an extension diploma upon successful completion.

Mechanical and Production Tool Design

An extension center full-time or part-time evening program of instruction requiring two semesters or the equivalent in part-time work and leading to the award of an extension diploma upon successful completion.

**Purdue University Technical Institutes**
(Lafayette, Indiana)

Building Construction Technology

An extension center full-time or part-time evening program requiring six terms during a period of two years or the equivalent part-time work and leading to the award of an associate technical aide diploma upon successful completion.

Drafting and Mechanical Technology

An extension center full-time or part-time evening program requiring six terms during a period of two years or the equivalent part-time work and leading to the award of an associate technical aide diploma upon successful completion.

Electrical Technology

An extension center full-time or part-time evening program requiring six terms during a period of two years or the equivalent part-time work and leading to the award of an associate technical aide diploma upon successful completion.

**RCA Institutes**
(New York)

Advanced Technology Course (Radio Communication and Sound and Television)

A resident full-time or part-time evening program of instruction requiring nine terms during a period of two years or the equivalent in part-time work and leading to the award of a certificate upon successful completion.

**Rochester Institute of Technology**
(Rochester, New York)

Electrical Technology

A resident full-time cooperative program of instruction requiring the equivalent of four semesters at the institution and forty weeks of industrial cooperative training and leading to the award of the degree of Associate in Applied Science.

Industrial Chemistry

A resident full-time cooperative program of instruction requiring the equivalent of four semesters at the institution and forty weeks of industrial cooperative training and leading to the award of the degree of Associate in Applied Science.

Mechanical Technology

A resident full-time cooperative program of instruction requiring the equivalent of four semesters at the institution and forty weeks of industrial cooperative training and leading to the award of the degree of Associate in Applied Science.

Photographic Technology

A resident full-time program of instruction in the materials and processes of photography for laboratories requiring chemical and sensitometric control, requiring four semesters and leading to the award of the degree of Associate in Applied Science.

**Southern Technical Institute**
(Chamblee, Georgia)

Building Construction Technology

A resident full-time or part-time evening program of instruction requiring six terms during a period of two years or the equivalent part-time work and leading to the award of an Associate in Science degree upon successful completion.

Civil Technology

A resident full-time or part-time evening program of instruction requiring six terms during a period of two years or the equivalent part-time work and leading to the award of an Associate in Science degree upon successful completion.

Electrical Technology

A resident full-time or part-time evening program of instruction requiring six terms during a period of two years or the equivalent part-time work and leading to the award of an Associate in Science degree upon successful completion.

Electronic and Radio Technology

A resident full-time or part-time evening program of instruction requiring six terms during a period of two years or the equivalent part-time work and leading to the award of an Associate in Science degree upon successful completion.

Gas and Fuel Technology

A resident full-time or part-time evening program of instruction requiring six terms during a period of two years or the equivalent part-time work and leading to the award of an Associate in Science degree upon successful completion.

Heating and Air-Conditioning Technology

A resident full-time or part-time evening program of instruction requiring six terms during a period of two years or the equivalent part-time work and leading to the award of an Associate in Science degree upon successful completion.

Industrial Technology

A resident full-time or part-time evening program of instruction requiring six terms during a period of two years or the equivalent part-time work and leading to the award of an Associate in Science degree upon successful completion.

Mechanical Technology

A resident full-time or part-time evening program of instruction requiring six terms during a period of two years or the equivalent part-time work and leading to the award of an Associate in Science degree upon successful completion.

**Spring Garden Institute**
(Philadelphia)

Electronic and Electrical Technology

A resident full-time program of instruction requiring four terms and leading to the award of a diploma upon successful completion.

Machine Designing

Terms 3 through 8 of a resident full-time course requiring six semesters and leading to the award of a diploma upon successful completion.

**TechRep Division—Philco Corporation**
(Philadelphia)

Basic and Advanced Electronics

A resident full-time program of instruction requiring the equivalent of one academic year and leading to the award of a certificate of achievement upon successful completion.

**University of Dayton—Technical Institute**
(Dayton, Ohio)

Electrical Technology

A resident full-time or part-time evening program of instruction requiring four semesters or the equivalent in part-time work and leading to the award of an Associate in Engineering degree.

Industrial Technology

A resident full-time or part-time evening program of instruction requiring four semesters or the equivalent in part-time work and leading to the award of an Associate in Engineering degree.

Mechanical Technology

A resident full-time or part-time evening program of instruction requiring four semesters or the equivalent in part-time work and leading to the award of an Associate in Engineering degree.

**Valparaiso Technical Institute**
(Valparaiso, Indiana)

Radio Technology

A resident full-time program of instruction requiring four terms during a period of one year and leading to the award of a diploma upon successful completion.

Advanced Radio Technology

A resident full-time program of instruction requiring six terms during a period of one and one-half years and leading to the award of a diploma upon successful completion.

Applied Radio Engineering

A resident full-time program of instruction requiring six terms during a period of one and one-half years and leading to the award of a diploma upon successful completion.

**Wentworth Institute**
(Boston)

Architectural Construction

A resident full-time program of instruction requiring four semesters and leading to the award of a certificate upon successful completion.

Industrial Electricity

A resident full-time program of instruction requiring four semesters and leading to the award of a certificate upon successful completion.

Industrial Electronics

A resident full-time program of instruction requiring four semesters and leading to the award of a certificate upon successful completion.

Machine Construction and Tool Design

A resident full-time program of instruction requiring four semesters and leading to the award of a certificate upon successful completion.

Steam and Diesel Engineering

A resident full-time program of instruction requiring four semesters and leading to the award of a certificate upon successful completion.

**West Virginia Institute of Technology**

(Montgomery, West Virginia)

Industrial Electricity

A resident full-time program of instruction requiring four semesters to the award of an Associate in the Applied Science of Industrial Electricity upon successful completion.

## Appendix 2. Dates of founding of technical institutes[1]

| Institute | Date of founding |
|---|---|
| *State and municipal:* | |
| Broome County Technical Institute, Binghamton, N.Y. | 1946 |
| California State Polytechnic College, San Luis Obispo, Calif. | 1901 |
| Connecticut State Technical Institute, Hartford, Conn. | 1946 |
| Erie County Technical Institute, Buffalo, N.Y. | 1946 |
| Fashion Institute of Technology, New York | 1944 |
| Hudson Valley Technical Institute, Troy, N.Y. | 1948 |
| Long Island Agricultural and Technical Institute, Farmingdale, N.Y. | 1930 |
| Mohawk Valley Technical Institute, Utica, N.Y. | 1946 |
| New Bedford Institute of Textiles and Technology, New Bedford, Mass. | 1946 |
| New Hampshire Technical Institute, Manchester, N.H. | 1946 |
| New Hampshire Technical Institute, Portsmouth, N.H. | 1945 |
| N.Y.C. Community College of Applied Arts and Science, Brooklyn | 1946 |

[1] Information obtained on Seventh Annual Survey of Technical Institutes made in January, 1951, and by personal correspondence in July, 1954.

| Institute | Date of founding |
|---|---|
| N.Y. State Agricultural and Technical Institute, Alfred, N.Y. | 1936 |
| N.Y. State Agricultural and Technical Institute, Canton, N.Y. | 1937 |
| N.Y. State Agricultural and Technical Institute, Delhi, N.Y. | 1937 |
| N.Y. State Agricultural and Technical Institute, Morrisville, N.Y. | 1942 |
| N.Y. State Institute of Agriculture and Home Economics, Cobleskill, N.Y. | 1911 |
| North Dakota State School of Science, Wahpeton, N.D. | 1921 |
| Oregon Technical Institute, Oretech, Ore. | 1947 |
| Putnam Technical School, Putnam, Conn. | 1945 |
| School of Industrial Art, Trenton, N.J. | 1898 |
| Westchester Community College, White Plains, N.Y. | 1946 |
| *Privately endowed:* | |
| Alliance Technical Institute, Cambridge Springs, Pa. | 1915 |
| Cogswell Polytechnical College, San Francisco | 1930 |
| Franklin Technical Institute, Boston | 1908 |
| LeTourneau Technical Institute, Longview, Tex. | 1946 |
| Mechanics Institute, New York | 1820 |
| Milwaukee School of Engineering, Milwaukee, Wis. | 1903 |
| Ohio Mechanics Institute, Cincinnati, Ohio | 1828 |
| Philadelphia Wireless Technical Institute, Philadelphia | 1945 |
| Rochester Institute of Technology, Rochester, N.Y. | 1829 |
| Spring Garden Institute, Philadelphia | 1851 |

| Institute | Date of founding |
|---|---|
| Wentworth Institute, Boston | 1911 |
| Wyomissing Polytechnic Institute, Wyomissing, Pa. | 1933 |
| *Extension divisions of colleges and universities:* | |
| College of William and Mary—Technical Institute, Norfolk, Va. | 1945 |
| Fenn College—Technical Institute, Cleveland, Ohio | 1937 |
| Lawrence Institute of Technology, Technical Institute Division, Detroit | 1950 |
| Lowell Institute School, Cambridge, Mass. | 1903 |
| New York University—Division of General Education, New York | 1945 |
| Oklahoma A. and M. College—School of Technical Training, Stillwater, Okla. | 1937 |
| Pennsylvania State University Technical Institutes, State College, Pa. | 1945 |
| Purdue University Technical Institutes, Lafayette, Ind. | 1943 |
| Southern Technical Institute, Chamblee, Ga. | 1948 |
| Temple University—Technical Institute and Community College, Philadelphia | 1945 |
| University of Dayton—Technical Institute, Dayton, Ohio | 1950 |
| University of Houston—College of Technology, Houston, Texas | 1948 |
| *Proprietary technical institutes:* | |
| Academy of Aeronautics, New York | 1939 |
| Acme School of Die Design Engineering, South Bend, Ind. | 1935 |
| Aeronautical University, Chicago | 1929 |

| Institute | Date of founding |
|---|---|
| American Television Institute of Technology, Chicago | 1934 |
| Bowman Technical School, Lancaster, Pa. | 1887 |
| *Cal-Aero Technical Institute, Glendale, Calif. | 1929 |
| Capitol Radio Engineering Institute, Washington | 1927 |
| Central Technical Institute, Kansas City, Mo. | 1914 |
| Chicago Technical College, Chicago | 1904 |
| Electronics Institute, Inc., Detroit | 1935 |
| Embry Riddle International School of Aviation, Miami | 1940 |
| Indianapolis Electronics School, Indianapolis, Ind. | 1947 |
| Industrial Trades Institute, Atlanta | 1948 |
| Lain Drafting College, Indianapolis, Ind. | 1941 |
| National Technical Institute, New York | 1940 |
| New England Technical Institute, Providence, R.I. | 1940 |
| Northrop Aeronautical Institute, Inglewood, Calif. | 1942 |
| Penn Technical Institute, Pittsburgh, Pa. | 1947 |
| Radio Television Institute Inc., New York | 1938 |
| RCA Institutes, Inc., New York | 1910 |
| Spartan School of Aeronautics, Tulsa, Okla. | 1940 |
| Valparaiso Technical Institute, Valparaiso, Ind. | 1934 |
| *YMCA schools:* | |
| Franklin University—Technical Institute, Columbus, Ohio | 1902 |
| Sinclair College, Dayton, Ohio | 1938 |
| *Canadian schools:* | |
| Ecole Provinciale de Papeterie, Trois Rivières, Que. | 1923 |
| Lakehead Technical Institute, Port Arthur, Ont. | 1948 |

* Discontinued operations in 1954.

| Institute | Date of founding |
| --- | --- |
| Montreal Technical School, Montreal, Que. | 1911 |
| Provincial Institute of Mining, Haileyburg, Ont. | 1945 |
| Provincial Institute of Technology and Art, Calgary, Alberta | 1916 |
| Provincial Institute of Textiles, Hamilton, Ont. | 1946 |
| Ryerson Institute of Technology, Toronto, Ont. | 1948 |

# Appendix 3. Full-time technical institute

TECHNOLOGICAL

| | Aeronautical Technology | | | | Air Conditioning, Heating, & Refrig. | Architecture, Bldg. Const., & Civil Technol. | | | | Automotive & Diesel Technology | Chemistry, Industrial |
|---|---|---|---|---|---|---|---|---|---|---|---|
| | Aircraft Design & Drafting | Aircraft & Eng. Maint. | Aircraft Technology | Aircraft Operations | | Architectural Drafting | Building Construction | Civil Technology | Structural Technology | | |
| *State and municipal institutes* | 2 | 21 | ... | 54 | 204 | 12 | 520 | 38 | 313 | 948 | 352 |
| Broome County Tech. Inst., Binghamton, N.Y. | ... | ... | ... | ... | ... | ... | ... | ... | ... | 15 | 33 |
| Conn. State Tech. Inst., Hartford | ... | ... | ... | ... | ... | ... | ... | ... | ... | ... | ... |
| Erie County Tech. Inst., Buffalo, N.Y. | ... | ... | ... | ... | ... | ... | 133 | ... | ... | ... | 95 |
| Fashion Inst. of Technol., New York | ... | ... | ... | ... | ... | ... | ... | ... | ... | ... | ... |
| Hudson Valley Tech. Inst., Troy, N.Y. | ... | ... | ... | ... | 41 | ... | ... | ... | 31 | 37 | ... |
| Long Island Agric. & Tech. Inst., Farmingdale, N.Y. | ... | ... | ... | 54 | 38 | ... | 68 | 38 | ... | 73 | 45 |
| Mohawk Valley Tech. Inst., Utica, N.Y. | ... | ... | ... | ... | ... | ... | ... | ... | ... | ... | ... |
| New Bedford Inst. of Textiles & Technol., Mass. | ... | ... | ... | ... | ... | ... | ... | ... | ... | ... | ... |
| N.H. Tech. Inst., Manchester | ... | ... | ... | ... | ... | ... | 16 | ... | ... | 29 | ... |
| N.H. Tech. Inst., Portsmouth | ... | ... | ... | ... | ... | ... | ... | ... | ... | 33 | ... |
| NYC Community College of Appl. Arts & Sci., Brooklyn | ... | ... | ... | ... | ... | ... | ... | ... | 259 | ... | 143 |
| NY State Agric. & Tech. Inst., Alfred | ... | ... | ... | ... | 40 | ... | 57 | ... | ... | 58 | ... |
| NY State Agric. & Tech. Inst., Canton | ... | ... | ... | ... | 42 | ... | ... | ... | ... | 17 | ... |
| NY State Agric. & Tech. Inst., Delhi | ... | ... | ... | ... | ... | ... | 93 | ... | ... | ... | ... |
| NY State Agric. & Tech. Inst., Morrisville | ... | ... | ... | ... | ... | ... | ... | ... | ... | 111 | ... |
| N. Dak. State School of Sci., Wahpeton | ... | ... | ... | ... | 43 | 5 | 49 | ... | ... | 237 | ... |
| Oregon Tech. Inst., Oretech | ... | ... | ... | ... | ... | ... | ... | ... | 23 | 338 | ... |
| Putnam Tech. Inst., Putnam, Conn. | 2 | 21 | ... | ... | ... | 7 | 7 | ... | ... | ... | ... |
| Westchester Community College, White Plains, N.Y. | ... | ... | ... | ... | ... | ... | 97 | ... | ... | ... | 36 |

## enrollment by curriculums, 1954–1955

CURRICULUMS

| Electrical Technology | | | | | | | | Mechanical Technology | | | | | | | | | | Miscellaneous courses | | | | |
|---|---|---|---|---|---|---|---|---|---|---|---|---|---|---|---|---|---|---|---|---|---|---|
| Elec. Const. & Wiring | Electrical Technology | Industrial Electronics | Radio & Television | Fire Protection Technology | Food Processing Technology | Gas Fuel Technology | Industrial Technology | Drafting & Machine Design | Instrumentation | Mechanical Technology | Steam & Diesel Technology | Tool & Die Making or Design | Tool Engng. Technology | Welding Technology | Metallurgical Technology | Optical Technology | Textile Technology | Machine Shop | Sheet Metal | Watch & Jewelry Technology | Other courses | Total |
| ... | 1370 | 61 | 314 | ... | 104 | ... | 75 | 126 | 76 | 944 | ... | 34 | 33 | 29 | 75 | 50 | 23 | 24 | 17 | 18 | 22 | 5859 |
| ... | 108 | ... | ... | ... | ... | ... | ... | ... | ... | 74 | ... | ... | ... | ... | ... | ... | ... | ... | ... | ... | ... | 230 |
| ... | 54 | ... | ... | ... | ... | ... | ... | ... | ... | 55 | ... | ... | 33 | ... | ... | ... | ... | ... | ... | ... | ... | 142 |
| ... | 137 | ... | ... | ... | ... | ... | ... | ... | ... | 149 | ... | ... | ... | ... | 75 | 50 | ... | ... | ... | ... | ... | 639 |
| ... | ... | ... | ... | ... | ... | ... | 64 | ... | ... | ... | ... | ... | ... | ... | ... | ... | ... | ... | ... | ... | ... | 64 |
| ... | 194 | ... | ... | ... | ... | ... | ... | ... | ... | 36 | ... | ... | ... | ... | ... | ... | ... | ... | ... | ... | ... | 339 |
| ... | 91 | ... | 30 | ... | ... | ... | ... | ... | 16 | 90 | ... | ... | ... | ... | ... | ... | ... | ... | ... | ... | ... | 543 |
| ... | 90 | ... | ... | ... | ... | ... | ... | ... | ... | 66 | ... | ... | ... | ... | ... | ... | ... | ... | ... | ... | ... | 156 |
| ... | ... | 34 | ... | ... | ... | ... | ... | 11 | ... | ... | ... | ... | ... | ... | ... | ... | 23 | ... | ... | ... | 5 | 73 |
| ... | 19 | ... | 41 | ... | ... | ... | ... | 35 | ... | ... | ... | ... | ... | 6 | ... | ... | ... | 24 | 17 | ... | ... | 187 |
| ... | ... | 27 | ... | ... | ... | ... | ... | 25 | ... | ... | ... | 34 | ... | 2 | ... | ... | ... | ... | ... | ... | ... | 121 |
| ... | 230 | ... | ... | ... | ... | ... | ... | ... | ... | 279 | ... | ... | ... | ... | ... | ... | ... | ... | ... | ... | ... | 911 |
| ... | 71 | ... | 58 | ... | ... | ... | 11 | ... | ... | 56 | ... | ... | ... | ... | ... | ... | ... | ... | ... | ... | ... | 351 |
| ... | 71 | ... | ... | ... | ... | ... | ... | 52 | ... | ... | ... | ... | ... | ... | ... | ... | ... | ... | ... | ... | ... | 182 |
| ... | ... | ... | ... | ... | ... | ... | ... | ... | ... | ... | ... | ... | ... | ... | ... | ... | ... | ... | ... | ... | ... | 93 |
| ... | 45 | ... | ... | ... | 104 | ... | ... | ... | 24 | ... | ... | ... | ... | ... | ... | ... | ... | ... | ... | 18 | ... | 302 |
| ... | 72 | ... | 90 | ... | ... | ... | ... | ... | ... | ... | ... | ... | ... | 6 | ... | ... | ... | ... | ... | ... | 17 | 519 |
| ... | 43 | ... | 95 | ... | ... | ... | ... | ... | 36 | 46 | ... | ... | ... | 15 | ... | ... | ... | ... | ... | ... | ... | 596 |
| ... | ... | ... | ... | ... | ... | ... | ... | 3 | ... | ... | ... | ... | ... | ... | ... | ... | ... | ... | ... | ... | ... | 40 |
| ... | 145 | ... | ... | ... | ... | ... | ... | ... | ... | 93 | ... | ... | ... | ... | ... | ... | ... | ... | ... | ... | ... | 371 |

| | Aeronautical Technology | | | | | Architecture, Bldg. Const., & Civil Technol. | | | | | |
|---|---|---|---|---|---|---|---|---|---|---|---|
| | Aircraft Design & Drafting | Aircraft & Eng. Maint. | Aircraft Technology | Aircraft Operations | Air Conditioning, Heating, & Refrig. | Architectural Drafting | Building Construction | Civil Technology | Structural Technology | Automotive & Diesel Technology | Chemistry, Industrial |
| *Privately endowed institutes* | ... | 68 | ... | ... | 158 | 133 | 160 | ... | 31 | 320 | 88 |
| Alliance Tech. Inst., Cambridge Springs, Pa | ... | ... | ... | ... | ... | ... | ... | ... | ... | ... | ... |
| Cogswell Polytech. College, San Francisco | ... | ... | ... | ... | ... | ... | ... | ... | 23 | ... | ... |
| Franklin Tech. Inst., Boston | ... | ... | ... | ... | ... | 28 | ... | ... | 8 | 40 | 5 |
| LeTourneau Tech. Inst., Longview, Texas | ... | ... | ... | ... | ... | ... | 24 | ... | ... | 40 | ... |
| Milwaukee School of Engng | ... | ... | ... | ... | 141 | ... | ... | ... | ... | ... | ... |
| Multnomah College Tech. Div., Portland, Ore | ... | ... | ... | ... | ... | ... | ... | ... | ... | 90 | ... |
| Ohio Mechanics Inst., Cincinnati | ... | ... | ... | ... | ... | ... | 35 | ... | ... | ... | 15 |
| Philadelphia Wireless Tech. Inst | ... | ... | ... | ... | ... | ... | ... | ... | ... | ... | ... |
| Rochester Inst. of Technol., Rochester, N.Y | ... | ... | ... | ... | ... | ... | ... | ... | ... | ... | 68 |
| Spring Garden Inst., Philadelphia | ... | ... | ... | ... | 17 | ... | ... | ... | ... | 150 | ... |
| Wentworth Inst., Boston | ... | 68 | ... | ... | ... | 105 | 101 | ... | ... | ... | ... |
| *YMCA schools* | ... | ... | ... | ... | ... | ... | ... | ... | ... | ... | ... |
| Franklin Univ. Tech. Inst., Columbus, Ohio | ... | ... | ... | ... | ... | ... | ... | ... | ... | ... | ... |
| Sinclair College, Dayton, Ohio | ... | ... | ... | ... | ... | ... | ... | ... | ... | ... | ... |

| Electrical Technology | | | | | | | | Mechanical Technology | | | | | | | | | | Miscellaneous courses | | | | |
|---|---|---|---|---|---|---|---|---|---|---|---|---|---|---|---|---|---|---|---|---|---|---|
| Elec. Const. & Wiring | Electrical Technology | Industrial Electronics | Radio & Television | Fire Protection Technology | Food Processing Technology | Gas Fuel Technology | Industrial Technology | Drafting & Machine Design | Instrumentation | Mechanical Technology | Steam & Diesel Technology | Tool & Die Making or Design | Tool Engng. Technology | Welding Technology | Metallurgical Technology | Optical Technology | Textile Technology | Machine Shop | Sheet Metal | Watch & Jewelry Technology | Other courses | Total |
| 33 | 421 | 571 | 507 | ... | ... | ... | 24 | 330 | ... | 548 | 62 | 100 | 14 | 30 | 4 | ... | ... | 94 | ... | ... | 55 | 3751 |
| ... | 4 | ... | ... | ... | ... | ... | ... | 5 | ... | ... | ... | 25 | 10 | ... | ... | ... | ... | ... | ... | ... | ... | 44 |
| ... | ... | 35 | ... | ... | ... | ... | ... | 21 | ... | ... | ... | ... | ... | ... | ... | ... | ... | ... | ... | ... | ... | 79 |
| 33 | 6 | 13 | ... | ... | ... | ... | 24 | 2 | ... | 14 | 3 | ... | ... | ... | ... | ... | ... | ... | ... | ... | ... | 176 |
| ... | 5 | ... | ... | ... | ... | ... | ... | 185 | ... | 115 | 5 | ... | 4 | 20 | 4 | ... | ... | ... | ... | ... | ... | 402 |
| ... | 67 | 413 | 341 | ... | ... | ... | ... | ... | ... | 109 | ... | ... | ... | 10 | ... | ... | ... | ... | ... | ... | 55 | 1136 |
| ... | ... | ... | 75 | ... | ... | ... | ... | ... | ... | 43 | ... | ... | ... | ... | ... | ... | ... | ... | ... | ... | ... | 208 |
| ... | 89 | ... | ... | ... | ... | ... | ... | ... | ... | 90 | ... | ... | ... | ... | ... | ... | ... | ... | ... | ... | ... | 229 |
| ... | ... | ... | 81 | ... | ... | ... | ... | ... | ... | ... | ... | ... | ... | ... | ... | ... | ... | ... | ... | ... | ... | 81 |
| ... | 175 | ... | ... | ... | ... | ... | ... | ... | ... | 177 | ... | ... | ... | ... | ... | ... | ... | ... | ... | ... | ... | 420 |
| ... | 22 | ... | 10 | ... | ... | ... | ... | 70 | ... | ... | ... | ... | ... | ... | ... | ... | ... | 27 | ... | ... | ... | 296 |
| ... | 53 | 110 | ... | ... | ... | ... | ... | 47 | ... | ... | 54 | 75 | ... | ... | ... | ... | ... | 67 | ... | ... | ... | 680 |
| ... | ... | ... | 65 | ... | ... | ... | 31 | 6 | ... | ... | ... | ... | ... | ... | ... | ... | ... | ... | ... | ... | ... | 102 |
| ... | ... | ... | 65 | ... | ... | ... | ... | 6 | ... | ... | ... | ... | ... | ... | ... | ... | ... | ... | ... | ... | ... | 71 |
| ... | ... | ... | ... | ... | ... | ... | 31 | ... | ... | ... | ... | ... | ... | ... | ... | ... | ... | ... | ... | ... | ... | 31 |

| | Aeronautical Technology | | | | | Architecture, Bldg. Const., & Civil Technol. | | | | | |
|---|---|---|---|---|---|---|---|---|---|---|---|
| | Aircraft Design & Drafting | Aircraft & Eng. Maint. | Aircraft Technology | Aircraft Operations | Air Conditioning, Heating, & Refrig. | Architectural Drafting | Building Construction | Civil Technology | Structural Technology | Automotive & Diesel Technology | Chemistry, Industrial |
| *Extension divisions of colleges and universities* | ... | 29 | ... | ... | 401 | 19 | 182 | 37 | ... | 139 | 6 |
| College of William & Mary Tech. Inst., Norfolk, Va | ... | ... | ... | ... | 25 | 5 | ... | ... | ... | 20 | ... |
| Hillyer College—Ward School of Electronics, Hartford | ... | ... | ... | ... | ... | ... | ... | ... | ... | ... | ... |
| Okla. A&M College—School of Tech. Training, Stillwater | ... | 23 | ... | ... | 43 | ... | 15 | ... | ... | 41 | ... |
| Penn State Univ. Tech. Inst., University Park | ... | ... | ... | ... | ... | ... | ... | ... | ... | ... | ... |
| Purdue Univ. Tech. Inst., Lafayette, Ind | ... | 6 | ... | ... | ... | ... | 33 | ... | ... | ... | 6 |
| Southern Ill. Univ. Vocational-Tech. Inst., Carbondale | ... | ... | ... | ... | ... | 14 | ... | ... | ... | 63 | ... |
| Southern Tech. Inst., Chamblee, Ga | ... | ... | ... | ... | 71 | ... | 74 | 37 | ... | ... | ... |
| Temple Univ. Tech. Inst. & Community College, Philadelphia | ... | ... | ... | ... | 40 | ... | 60 | ... | ... | ... | ... |
| Univ. of Dayton College of Technol. | ... | ... | ... | ... | ... | ... | ... | ... | ... | ... | ... |
| Univ. of Houston Tech. Inst | ... | ... | ... | ... | 222 | ... | ... | ... | ... | ... | ... |
| W. Va. Inst. of Technol., Montgomery | ... | ... | ... | ... | ... | ... | ... | ... | ... | 15 | ... |

CURRICULUMS (*Continued*)

| Electrical Technology | | | | | | | | Mechanical Technology | | | | | | | | | | Miscellaneous courses | | | | |
|---|---|---|---|---|---|---|---|---|---|---|---|---|---|---|---|---|---|---|---|---|---|---|
| Elec. Const. & Wiring | Electrical Technology | Industrial Electronics | Radio & Television | Fire Protection Technology | Food Processing Technology | Gas Fuel Technology | Industrial Technology | Drafting & Machine Design | Instrumentation | Mechanical Technology | Steam & Diesel Technology | Tool & Die Making or Design | Tool Engng. Technology | Welding Technology | Metallurgical Technology | Optical Technology | Textile Technology | Machine Shop | Sheet Metal | Watch & Jewelry Technology | Other courses | Total |
| ... | 1040 | 103 | 845 | 47 | ... | 41 | 71 | 249 | 26 | 635 | 331 | ... | 16 | 34 | 5 | ... | ... | 94 | ... | ... | 2 | 4352 |
| ... | ... | ... | 92 | ... | ... | ... | ... | 26 | ... | ... | ... | ... | ... | ... | ... | ... | ... | ... | ... | ... | ... | 168 |
| ... | ... | 28 | 172 | ... | ... | ... | ... | ... | 26 | ... | ... | ... | ... | ... | ... | ... | ... | ... | ... | ... | ... | 226 |
| ... | 51 | ... | 52 | 47 | ... | ... | ... | 34 | ... | ... | 86 | ... | ... | 12 | ... | ... | ... | 16 | ... | ... | ... | 420 |
| ... | 405 | ... | 47 | ... | ... | ... | ... | ... | ... | 408 | ... | ... | ... | ... | ... | ... | ... | ... | ... | ... | ... | 860 |
| ... | 13 | ... | 29 | ... | ... | ... | 12 | ... | ... | 29 | ... | ... | 16 | ... | 5 | ... | ... | ... | ... | ... | ... | 149 |
| ... | ... | ... | 69 | ... | ... | ... | ... | 13 | ... | ... | ... | ... | ... | 22 | ... | ... | ... | 78 | ... | ... | ... | 259 |
| ... | 62 | ... | 176 | ... | ... | 41 | 44 | ... | ... | 96 | ... | ... | ... | ... | ... | ... | ... | ... | ... | ... | ... | 601 |
| ... | 375 | ... | ... | ... | ... | ... | ... | ... | ... | 50 | ... | ... | ... | ... | ... | ... | ... | ... | ... | ... | ... | 525 |
| ... | 32 | ... | ... | ... | ... | ... | 15 | ... | ... | 52 | ... | ... | ... | ... | ... | ... | ... | ... | ... | ... | 2 | 101 |
| ... | 80 | 75 | 208 | ... | ... | ... | ... | 176 | ... | ... | 245 | ... | ... | ... | ... | ... | ... | ... | ... | ... | ... | 1006 |
| ... | 22 | ... | ... | ... | ... | ... | ... | ... | ... | ... | ... | ... | ... | ... | ... | ... | ... | ... | ... | ... | ... | 37 |

| | Aeronautical Technology | | | | | Architecture, Bldg. Const., & Civil Technol. | | | | | |
|---|---|---|---|---|---|---|---|---|---|---|---|
| | Aircraft Design & Drafting | Aircraft & Eng. Maint. | Aircraft Technology | Aircraft Operations | Air Conditioning, Heating, & Refrig. | Architectural Drafting | Building Construction | Civil Technology | Structural Technology | Automotive & Diesel Technology | Chemistry, Industrial |
| *Proprietary institutes* | 104 | 1236 | 614 | ... | 102 | 132 | 29 | 50 | ... | ... | ... |
| Academy of Aeronautics, New York | 99 | 331 | 129 | ... | ... | ... | ... | ... | ... | ... | ... |
| Acme School of Die Design Engng., South Bend, Ind | ... | ... | ... | ... | ... | ... | ... | ... | ... | ... | ... |
| Aeronautical Univ., Chicago | 5 | 120 | 30 | ... | ... | ... | ... | ... | ... | ... | ... |
| American Television Inst. of Tech., Chicago | ... | ... | ... | ... | ... | ... | ... | ... | ... | ... | ... |
| Bowman Tech. School, Lancaster, Pa | ... | ... | ... | ... | ... | ... | ... | ... | ... | ... | ... |
| Capitol Radio Engng. Inst., Washington | ... | ... | ... | ... | ... | ... | ... | ... | ... | ... | ... |
| Central Tech. Inst., Kansas City, Mo | ... | ... | ... | ... | ... | ... | ... | ... | ... | ... | ... |
| Chicago Tech. College | ... | ... | ... | ... | ... | 100 | 29 | 50 | ... | ... | ... |
| Detroit Engng. Inst | ... | ... | ... | ... | ... | ... | ... | ... | ... | ... | ... |
| Electronics Inst., Detroit | ... | ... | ... | ... | ... | ... | ... | ... | ... | ... | ... |
| Indianapolis Electronics School | ... | ... | ... | ... | ... | ... | ... | ... | ... | ... | ... |
| Lain Drafting College, Indianapolis | ... | ... | ... | ... | ... | 32 | ... | ... | ... | ... | ... |
| New England Tech. Inst., Providence and Hartford | ... | ... | ... | ... | 102 | ... | ... | ... | ... | ... | ... |
| Northrop Aeronautical Inst., Inglewood, Calif. | ... | 430 | 455 | ... | ... | ... | ... | ... | ... | ... | ... |
| Penn Tech. Inst., Pittsburgh | ... | ... | ... | ... | ... | ... | ... | ... | ... | ... | ... |
| RCA Institutes, Inc., New York | ... | ... | ... | ... | ... | ... | ... | ... | ... | ... | ... |
| Spartan School of Aeronautics, Tulsa, Okla | ... | 355 | ... | ... | ... | ... | ... | ... | ... | ... | ... |
| Valparaiso Tech. Inst., Valparaiso, Ind | ... | ... | ... | ... | ... | ... | ... | ... | ... | ... | ... |
| Grand total, technological | 106 | 1354 | 614 | 54 | 865 | 296 | 891 | 125 | 344 | 1407 | 446 |
| No. of curriculums | 3 | 8 | 3 | 1 | 13 | 8 | 16 | 3 | 5 | 18 | 9 |

SOURCE: Eleventh Annual Survey of Technical Institutes, 1954–

CURRICULUMS (*Continued*)

| Electrical Technology | | | | | | | | Mechanical Technology | | | | | | | | | | Miscellaneous courses | | | | |
|---|---|---|---|---|---|---|---|---|---|---|---|---|---|---|---|---|---|---|---|---|---|---|
| Elec. Const. & Wiring | Electrical Technology | Industrial Electronics | Radio & Television | Fire Protection Technology | Food Processing Technology | Gas Fuel Technology | Industrial Technology | Drafting & Machine Design | Instrumentation | Mechanical Technology | Steam & Diesel Technology | Tool & Die Making or Design | Tool Engng. Technology | Welding Technology | Metallurgical Technology | Optical Technology | Textile Technology | Machine Shop | Sheet Metal | Watch & Jewelry Technology | Other courses | Total |
| 2 | 85 | ... | 3019 | .. | ... | .. | 8 | 21 | ... | 172 | ... | 232 | ... | 65 | ... | ... | ... | ... | ... | 80 | ... | 5951 |
| .. | ... | ... | ... | .. | ... | .. | ... | ... | ... | ... | ... | ... | ... | ... | ... | ... | ... | ... | ... | ... | ... | 559 |
| .. | ... | ... | ... | .. | ... | .. | ... | ... | ... | ... | ... | 232 | ... | ... | ... | ... | ... | ... | ... | ... | ... | 232 |
| .. | ... | ... | ... | .. | ... | .. | ... | ... | ... | ... | ... | ... | ... | ... | ... | ... | ... | ... | ... | ... | ... | 155 |
| .. | ... | ... | 325 | .. | ... | .. | ... | ... | ... | ... | ... | ... | ... | ... | ... | ... | ... | ... | ... | ... | ... | 325 |
| .. | ... | ... | ... | .. | ... | .. | ... | ... | ... | ... | ... | ... | ... | ... | ... | ... | ... | ... | ... | 80 | ... | 80 |
| .. | ... | ... | 310 | .. | ... | .. | ... | ... | ... | ... | ... | ... | ... | ... | ... | ... | ... | ... | ... | ... | ... | 310 |
| .. | ... | ... | 525 | .. | ... | .. | ... | ... | ... | ... | ... | ... | ... | ... | ... | ... | ... | ... | ... | ... | ... | 525 |
| 2 | 85 | ... | 2 | .. | ... | .. | ... | 21 | ... | 117 | ... | ... | ... | 15 | ... | ... | ... | ... | ... | ... | ... | 421 |
| .. | ... | ... | ... | .. | ... | .. | ... | ... | ... | 55 | ... | ... | ... | ... | ... | ... | ... | ... | ... | ... | ... | 55 |
| .. | ... | ... | 605 | .. | ... | .. | ... | ... | ... | ... | ... | ... | ... | ... | ... | ... | ... | ... | ... | ... | ... | 605 |
| .. | ... | ... | 78 | .. | ... | .. | ... | ... | ... | ... | ... | ... | ... | ... | ... | ... | ... | ... | ... | ... | ... | 78 |
| .. | ... | ... | ... | .. | ... | .. | 8 | ... | ... | ... | ... | ... | ... | 50 | ... | ... | ... | ... | ... | ... | ... | 90 |
| .. | ... | ... | 148 | .. | ... | .. | ... | ... | ... | ... | ... | ... | ... | ... | ... | ... | ... | ... | ... | ... | ... | 250 |
| .. | ... | ... | ... | .. | ... | .. | ... | ... | ... | ... | ... | ... | ... | ... | ... | ... | ... | ... | ... | ... | ... | 885 |
| .. | ... | ... | 197 | .. | ... | .. | ... | ... | ... | ... | ... | ... | ... | ... | ... | ... | ... | ... | ... | ... | ... | 197 |
| .. | ... | ... | 493 | .. | ... | .. | ... | ... | ... | ... | ... | ... | ... | ... | ... | ... | ... | ... | ... | ... | ... | 493 |
| .. | ... | ... | ... | .. | ... | .. | ... | ... | ... | ... | ... | ... | ... | ... | ... | ... | ... | ... | ... | ... | ... | 355 |
| .. | ... | ... | 336 | .. | ... | .. | ... | ... | ... | ... | ... | ... | ... | ... | ... | ... | ... | ... | ... | ... | ... | 336 |
| 35 | 2916 | 735 | 4750 | 47 | 104 | 41 | 209 | 732 | 102 | 2299 | 393 | 366 | 128 | 93 | 84 | 50 | 23 | 212 | 17 | 98 | 79 | 20,015 |
| 2 | 31 | 8 | 28 | 1 | 1 | 1 | 8 | 17 | 4 | 23 | 5 | 4 | 6 | 8 | 3 | 1 | 1 | 5 | 1 | 2 | 4 | 251 |

1955.

| | Agriculture | | | | |
|---|---|---|---|---|---|
| | Agric. Industries | Agric., General | Animal & Poultry Husbandry | Farm Power Machinery | Floriculture & Horticulture |
| *State and municipal institutes* | 197 | 542 | 160 | 63 | 212 |
| Broome County Tech. Inst., Binghamton, N.Y. | ... | ... | ... | ... | ... |
| Calif. State Polytech. College, San Luis Obispo | ... | 158 | ... | ... | ... |
| Erie County Tech. Inst., Buffalo, N.Y. | ... | ... | ... | ... | ... |
| Fashion Inst. of Technol., New York | ... | ... | ... | ... | ... |
| Long Island Agric. & Tech. Inst., Farmingdale, N.Y. | ... | 226 | ... | ... | 138 |
| Mohawk Valley Tech. Inst., Utica, N.Y. | ... | ... | ... | ... | ... |
| N.H. Tech. Inst., Manchester | ... | ... | ... | ... | ... |
| NYC Community College of Appl. Arts & Sci., Brooklyn | ... | ... | ... | ... | ... |
| NY State Agric. & Tech. Inst., Alfred | 38 | 29 | 54 | 63 | 43 |
| NY State Agric. & Tech. Inst., Canton | 15 | 33 | ... | ... | ... |
| NY State Agric. & Tech. Inst., Delhi | 71 | ... | ... | ... | ... |
| NY State Agric. & Tech. Inst., Morrisville | 32 | 37 | 48 | ... | 15 |
| NY State Inst. of Agric. & Home Ec., Cobleskill | 41 | 20 | 58 | ... | 16 |
| N. Dak. State School of Sci., Wahpeton | ... | ... | ... | ... | ... |
| Ore. Tech. Inst., Oretech | ... | 39 | ... | ... | ... |
| Westchester Community College, White Plains, N.Y. | ... | ... | ... | ... | ... |

THAN TECHNOLOGICAL

| Business | | | | | | | | | Graphic Arts | | | Health Services | | | | | Home Economics | | | |
|---|---|---|---|---|---|---|---|---|---|---|---|---|---|---|---|---|---|---|---|---|
| Business, General | Executive Assisting | Hotel Technology | Retail Distribution | Sales, Industrial | Secretarial | Tech. Office Assisting | Apparel Technology | Textile Design | Appl. Art & Advertising | Photography | Publishing & Printing | Dental Hygiene | Dental Lab. Technology | Medical Lab. Technology | Medical Office Assisting | Practical Nursing | Clothing & Textiles | Food Administration | Miscellaneous | Total |
| 340 | 396 | 241 | 324 | 159 | 205 | 182 | 277 | 64 | 356 | ... | 44 | 346 | 123 | 241 | 171 | 62 | 21 | 244 | 428 | 5396 |
| ... | ... | ... | ... | ... | ... | 33 | ... | ... | ... | ... | ... | ... | ... | ... | 24 | ... | ... | ... | ... | 57 |
| ... | ... | ... | ... | ... | ... | ... | ... | ... | ... | ... | ... | ... | ... | ... | ... | ... | ... | ... | ... | 158 |
| ... | ... | ... | ... | ... | ... | ... | ... | ... | ... | ... | ... | 97 | ... | ... | ... | ... | ... | 54 | ... | 151 |
| ... | ... | ... | ... | ... | ... | ... | 277 | 64 | ... | ... | ... | ... | ... | ... | ... | ... | ... | ... | ... | 341 |
| ... | 27 | ... | ... | ... | ... | 77 | ... | ... | 80 | ... | ... | 72 | ... | ... | ... | ... | ... | ... | ... | 620 |
| ... | ... | ... | 101 | ... | ... | ... | ... | ... | ... | ... | ... | ... | ... | ... | ... | ... | ... | ... | ... | 101 |
| ... | ... | ... | ... | ... | ... | ... | ... | ... | 13 | ... | ... | ... | ... | ... | ... | ... | ... | ... | ... | 13 |
| ... | 274 | 218 | 223 | 146 | ... | ... | ... | ... | 247 | ... | ... | 177 | 123 | 141 | ... | ... | ... | ... | 83 | 1632 |
| 182 | ... | ... | ... | ... | 144 | ... | ... | ... | ... | ... | ... | ... | ... | 64 | 80 | ... | ... | ... | 87 | 784 |
| ... | ... | 23 | ... | ... | ... | 65 | ... | ... | ... | ... | ... | ... | ... | ... | ... | ... | 21 | 38 | ... | 195 |
| ... | ... | ... | ... | ... | 22 | ... | ... | ... | ... | ... | ... | ... | ... | ... | ... | ... | ... | 25 | ... | 118 |
| ... | ... | ... | ... | ... | ... | ... | ... | ... | ... | ... | ... | ... | ... | ... | ... | 32 | ... | 62 | ... | 226 |
| 43 | ... | ... | ... | ... | ... | ... | ... | ... | ... | ... | ... | ... | ... | ... | ... | ... | ... | 35 | 68 | 281 |
| 76 | ... | ... | ... | ... | 33 | ... | ... | ... | ... | ... | 44 | ... | ... | ... | ... | 16 | ... | 9 | 63 | 241 |
| 39 | ... | ... | ... | 11 | 6 | 7 | ... | ... | 16 | ... | ... | ... | ... | 36 | ... | 14 | ... | ... | 127 | 295 |
| ... | 95 | ... | ... | ... | ... | ... | ... | ... | ... | ... | ... | ... | ... | ... | 67 | ... | ... | 21 | ... | 183 |

| | Agricultural | | | | |
|---|---|---|---|---|---|
| | Agric. Industries | Agric., General | Animal & Poultry Husbandry | Farm Power Machinery | Floriculture & Horticulture |
| *Privately endowed institutes* | ... | ... | ... | ... | ... |
| Franklin Tech. Inst., Boston | ... | ... | ... | ... | ... |
| LeTourneau Tech. Inst., Longview, Tex | ... | ... | ... | ... | ... |
| Rochester Inst. of Technol., Rochester, N.Y | ... | ... | ... | ... | ... |
| Spring Garden Inst., Philadelphia | ... | ... | ... | ... | ... |
| *Extension divisions of colleges and universities* | ... | ... | ... | ... | ... |
| Penn State Univ. Tech. Inst., University Park | ... | ... | ... | ... | ... |
| Purdue Univ. Tech. Inst., Lafayette, Ind | ... | ... | ... | ... | ... |
| Southern Ill. Univ. Vocational-Tech. Inst., Carbondale | ... | ... | ... | ... | ... |
| W. Va. Inst. of Technol., Montgomery | ... | ... | ... | ... | ... |
| *Proprietary institute:* Central Tech. Inst., Kansas City, Mo | ... | ... | ... | ... | ... |
| *YMCA school:* Sinclair College, Dayton, Ohio | ... | ... | ... | ... | ... |
| Grand total, other than technological | 197 | 542 | 160 | 63 | 212 |
| Number of curriculums | 5 | 7 | 3 | 1 | 4 |

SOURCE: Eleventh Annual Survey of Technical Institutes, 1954–

THAN TECHNOLOGICAL (*Continued*)

| Business | | | | | | | | | Graphic Arts | | | Health Services | | | | | Home Economics | | | |
|---|---|---|---|---|---|---|---|---|---|---|---|---|---|---|---|---|---|---|---|---|
| Business, General | Executive Assisting | Hotel Technology | Retail Distribution | Sales, Industrial | Secretarial | Tech. Office Assisting | Apparel Technology | Textile Design | Appl. Art & Advertising | Photography | Publishing & Printing | Dental Hygiene | Dental Lab. Technology | Medical Lab. Technology | Medical Office Assisting | Practical Nursing | Clothing & Textiles | Food Administration | Miscellaneous | Total |
| 145 | ... | ... | 149 | ... | ... | ... | ... | ... | 85 | 167 | 204 | ... | ... | ... | ... | ... | 19 | 38 | 66 | 873 |
| ... | ... | ... | ... | ... | ... | ... | ... | ... | ... | 8 | ... | ... | ... | ... | ... | ... | ... | ... | 33 | 41 |
| ... | ... | ... | ... | ... | ... | ... | ... | ... | ... | ... | 6 | ... | ... | ... | ... | ... | ... | ... | ... | 6 |
| 145 | ... | ... | 149 | ... | ... | ... | ... | ... | 85 | 159 | 198 | ... | ... | ... | ... | ... | ... | 38 | 33 | 807 |
| ... | ... | ... | ... | ... | ... | ... | ... | ... | ... | ... | ... | ... | ... | ... | ... | ... | 19 | ... | ... | 19 |
| 47 | ... | ... | 15 | ... | 122 | ... | ... | ... | ... | ... | 7 | ... | ... | ... | ... | 39 | ... | ... | 26 | 256 |
| ... | ... | ... | ... | ... | 42 | ... | ... | ... | ... | ... | ... | ... | ... | ... | ... | ... | ... | ... | ... | 42 |
| ... | ... | ... | ... | ... | ... | ... | ... | ... | ... | ... | ... | ... | ... | ... | ... | 39 | ... | ... | 6 | 45 |
| 47 | ... | ... | 15 | ... | 57 | ... | ... | ... | ... | ... | 7 | ... | ... | ... | ... | ... | ... | ... | 20 | 146 |
| ... | ... | ... | ... | ... | 23 | ... | ... | ... | ... | ... | ... | ... | ... | ... | ... | ... | ... | ... | ... | 23 |
| ... | ... | ... | ... | ... | ... | ... | ... | ... | ... | ... | ... | ... | ... | ... | ... | ... | ... | ... | 202 | 202 |
| 24 | ... | ... | ... | ... | ... | ... | ... | ... | ... | ... | ... | ... | ... | ... | ... | ... | ... | ... | ... | 24 |
| 556 | 396 | 241 | 488 | 157 | 327 | 182 | 277 | 64 | 441 | 167 | 255 | 346 | 123 | 241 | 171 | 101 | 40 | 282 | 722 | 6751 |
| 7 | 3 | 2 | 4 | 2 | 7 | 4 | 1 | 1 | 5 | 2 | 4 | 3 | 1 | 3 | 3 | 4 | 2 | 8 | 10 | 96 |

1955.

## Appendix 4. Check list of criteria for identifying technical jobs[1]

| | | *Classification* |
|---|---|---|
| | Technical | ________ |
| Job Title________________ | Subtechnical | ________ |
| | Trade | ________ |
| | Professional | ________ |

| A technical job: | Low High |
|---|---|
| 1. Emphasizes technical knowledge | 1 2 3 4 5 |
| 2. Emphasizes technical skill (the ability to use technical knowledge) | 1 2 3 4 5 |
| 3. Deals with rational processes as contrasted with empirical rules | 1 2 3 4 5 |
| 4. Has concern with cause and effect | 1 2 3 4 5 |
| 5. Emphasizes analysis and diagnosis | 1 2 3 4 5 |
| 6. Requires frequent exercise of ability to use involved judgment | 1 2 3 4 5 |
| 7. Deals with many factors and a large number of variables | 1 2 3 4 5 |
| 8. Contends with a large variety of situations | 1 2 3 4 5 |
| 9. Requires a knowledge of skilled work but not necessarily skill in doing it | 1 2 3 4 5 |
| 10. Requires a broad background of fundamental science and mathematics | 1 2 3 4 5 |

[1] J. Cayce Morrison, chairman, *A Guide to the Development of Programs for the Institutes of Applied Arts and Sciences,* University of the State of New York, Albany, 1946, p. 43.

| A technical job: | Low | | | | High |
|---|---|---|---|---|---|
| 11. Involves use of a variety of instruments | 1 | 2 | 3 | 4 | 5 |
| 12. Requires effective use of language to interpret orders and make reports | 1 | 2 | 3 | 4 | 5 |
| 13. Involves the element of leadership in supervisory occupations | 1 | 2 | 3 | 4 | 5 |
| 14. Requires understanding of industrial equipment and processes | 1 | 2 | 3 | 4 | 5 |
| 15. Frequently involves visualization of plans and drawings and a degree of creative design | 1 | 2 | 3 | 4 | 5 |

For each criterion circle the number you judge to represent the degree the job requires: 1—low; 5—high. Omit those criteria which are not applicable. An average score above 3 would indicate a technical job; below 3 a trade or subtechnical job. Technical jobs which usually require four years or more of formal education should be classified as professional.

# Appendix 5. Representative curriculums in technical institutes

## Academy of Aeronautics

### *Aircraft Design*

**Term I***

|  | Credit |
|---|---|
| Aircraft Design I | 1½ |
| Algebra and Trigonometry | 7½ |
| Physics I | 7 |
| Aircraft Construction | 11 |
| Aircraft Materials | 3½ |
| | 30½ |

**Term II**

|  | Credit |
|---|---|
| Aircraft Design II | 2½ |
| Engineering Drafting and Descriptive Geom. | 11 |
| Analytic Geometry and Calculus | 7½ |
| Physics II | 5 |
| Statics | 4 |
| | 30 |

**Term III**

|  | Credit |
|---|---|
| Aircraft Design III | 6 |
| Engineering Illustration | 4½ |
| Calculus and Differential Equations | 6 |
| Strength of Materials | 4 |
| Dynamics | 4 |
| Aircraft Electricity | 5 |
| | 29½ |

**Term IV**

|  | Credit |
|---|---|
| Aircraft Design IV | 7½ |
| Aerodynamics I | 6 |
| Engineering Lab I | 3½ |
| Aircraft Structures I | 6 |
| Aircraft Operating Systems | 5 |
| Technical Writing | 3 |
| | 31 |

**Term V**

|  | Credit |
|---|---|
| Aircraft Design V | 7½ |
| Aerodynamics II | 4 |
| Engineering Lab II | 3½ |
| Thermodynamics | 4 |
| Industrial Relations | 1½ |
| Aircraft Structures II | 4 |
| Aircraft Power Plants | 5 |
| | 29½ |

* Term is 22 weeks in length.

## Broome County Technical Institute

*Mechanical Technology*

| Term I* | Credit | Term II | Credit |
|---|---|---|---|
| Communication Skills | 3 | Communication Skills | 3 |
| Industrial Safety and First Aid | 2 | Psychology | 3 |
| Shop | 2 | Shop | 2 |
| Mathematics | 3 | Mathematics | 3 |
| Engineering Drawing | 2 | Engineering Drawing | 1 |
| Mechanics | 4 | Mechanics | 3 |
| | | Heat | 4 |
| | 16 | | 19 |

| Term III | | Term IV | |
|---|---|---|---|
| Communication Skills | 3 | Economics | 3 |
| Economics | 3 | Shop | 2 |
| Shop | 2 | Mathematics | 3 |
| Mathematics | 3 | Machine Design | 4 |
| Mechanisms | 4 | Mechanical Machines | 4 |
| Strength of Materials | 4 | Electricity | 4 |
| Metallurgy | 4 | Technical Reports | 1 |
| | 23 | | 21 |

| Term V | Credit |
|---|---|
| Advanced Processes | 2 |
| Production Design | 3 |
| Mechanical Machines | 4 |
| Quality Control | 4 |
| Electricity | 4 |
| Industrial Organization | 3 |
| | 20 |

* Term is 12 weeks in length.

## Central Technical Institute

*Electronics, Radio, and Television Technology*

**Semester I***

| Course | Clock hours per semester |
|---|---|
| Basic Radio, Theory | 300 |
| Basic Radio, Lab | 200 |
| Applied Radio Mathematics | 100 |
| | 600 |

**Semester II***

| Course | Clock hours per semester |
|---|---|
| Electronics, Theory | 300 |
| Electronics, Lab | 200 |
| Applied Radio Mathematics | 100 |
| | 600 |

**Semester III***

| Course | Clock hours per semester |
|---|---|
| Television, Theory | 300 |
| Television, Lab | 300 |
| | 600 |

**Semester IV†**

| Course | Clock hours per semester |
|---|---|
| Technical Drafting I | 60 |
| English | 60 |
| Announcing and Television Production | 120 |
| Studio Practice, Audio and Video | 120 |
| | 360 |

**Semester V‡**

| Course | Clock hours per semester |
|---|---|
| Mathematics I | 80 |
| Pulse Systems | 80 |
| Technical Drafting II | 80 |
| Ultra-high-frequency and Microwave Techniques | 48 |
| Television Optics | 32 |
| Test Equipment and Measurements | 80 |
| Measurements Lab | 80 |
| | 480 |

**Semester VI‡**

| Course | Clock hours per semester |
|---|---|
| Mathematics II | 80 |
| Television Engineering | 48 |
| Color Television | 32 |
| Technical Reports | 80 |
| Library Research | 80 |
| Frequency-Modulation Engineering | 80 |
| Electronic Circuit Drawing | 80 |
| | 480 |

* 20 weeks. † 12 weeks. ‡ 16 weeks.

## Oklahoma A and M College—School of Technical Training

*Fire Protection*

### First Year

| First Semester | Credit | Second Semester | Credit |
|---|---|---|---|
| Freshman Composition | 3 | Composition | 3 |
| General Chemistry | 4 | General Chemistry | 4 |
| Employment Relations | 2 | Technical Mathematics | 5 |
| Technical Drawing | 3 | Fire Fighting Practices | 1 |
| Fire Extinguisher Installation, Maintenance, and Recharge | 2 | Fire Protection | 2 |
| Fire Fighting Practices | 1 | Principles of Fire Inspection | 2 |
| Fire Hazards and Causes | 2 | | |
| | 17 | | 17 |

### Second Year

| First Semester | | Second Semester | |
|---|---|---|---|
| Essentials of Public Speaking | 2 | Fire and Marine Insurance | 3 |
| Essentials of Electricity | 4 | Light and Power Wiring | 4 |
| Elementary Practical Mechanics | 3 | Safety Engineering | 1 |
| Introductory Psychology | 3 | Industrial Safety | 3 |
| Fire Fighting Practices | 1 | Fire Fighting Tactics | 2 |
| Fire Prevention | 2 | Automatic Sprinkler Protection | 2 |
| Fire Inspection Practices | 2 | Fire Protection Hydraulics | 2 |
| | 17 | | 17 |

## Pennsylvania State University Technical Institutes

*Electrical Technology*

First Year

| First Semester | Credit | Second Semester | Credit |
|---|---|---|---|
| Engineering Drawing | 2 | Descriptive Geometry | 2 |
| English Grammar | 3 | Composition and Rhetoric | 3 |
| Orientation | 2 | D-C Circuits and Lab | 4 |
| Technical Calculations | 4 | Electrical Construction | 1 |
| Fundamentals of D-C Circuits | 4 | Algebra | 3 |
| Electrical Instrumentation | 2 | Elementary Mechanics | 3 |
| | 17 | | 16 |

Second Year

| First Semester | | Second Semester | |
|---|---|---|---|
| D-C Machines and Lab | 4 | A-C Machines and Lab | 4 |
| A-C Circuits and Lab | 4 | Electric Power Generating and Distribution | 2 |
| Elementary Electronics | 2 | Applied Electronics and Lab | 5 |
| Industrial Organization and Management | 2 | Industrial Relations | 2 |
| Plant Trigonometry | 3 | Economics of Industry | 2 |
| Public Speaking | 3 | Mechanisms | 2 |
| | 18 | | 17 |

## Purdue University Technical Institutes

### *Electrical Technology—Radio and Television Option*

First Year

| First Semester | Credit | Second Semester | Credit |
|---|---|---|---|
| Technical Drawing | 2 | Electrical Circuits | 5 |
| English Grammar and Composition | 2 | Technical Report Writing | 4 |
| Psychology | 2 | Mathematics: Trigonometry and Algebra | 4 |
| Mathematics: Geometry and Algebra | 4 | Slide Rule | 1 |
| Introductory Chemistry | 3 | Physics: Electricity and Heat | 4 |
| Physics: Mechanics and Heat | 4 | | |
| | 17 | | 18 |

Second Year

| First Semester | | Second Semester | |
|---|---|---|---|
| Electronics | 4 | Radio | 5 |
| Electrical Measurements | 4 | Television | 5 |
| Practical Speaking | 2 | Circuit Diagrams | 2 |
| Democratic Government | 2 | Human Relations in Industry | 2 |
| Industrial Organization and Production | 4 | Economics of Industry | 2 |
| | 16 | | 16 |

## Southern Technical Institute

*Building Construction*

**FIRST QUARTER***

| | Credit |
|---|---|
| Technical Drawing I | 2 |
| Composition and Rhetoric | 3 |
| Human Relations | 3 |
| Algebra | 6 |
| General Woodworking | 2 |
| | 16 |

**SECOND QUARTER**

| | Credit |
|---|---|
| Elementary Surveying | 6 |
| Composition and Rhetoric | 3 |
| Trigonometry and Analytics | 5 |
| Mechanics | 6 |
| | 20 |

**THIRD QUARTER**

| | |
|---|---|
| Graphics | 6 |
| Building Materials | 3 |
| Mechanics of Materials | 6 |
| Heat, Sound, and Light | 4 |
| | 19 |

**FOURTH QUARTER**

| | |
|---|---|
| Architectural History | 3 |
| Building Design I | 7 |
| Graphic Statics | 1 |
| Contracts and Specifications | 3 |
| Electricity | 6 |
| | 20 |

**FIFTH QUARTER**

| | |
|---|---|
| Building Design II | 6 |
| Wood and Steel Construction | 5 |
| Building Equipment | 3 |
| Structural Drafting | 2 |
| Public Speaking | 2 |
| | 18 |

**SIXTH QUARTER**

| | |
|---|---|
| Costs, Estimates | 4 |
| Building Design III | 6 |
| Concrete Construction | 5 |
| Technical Writing | 2 |
| Seminar | 1 |
| | 18 |

* Quarters are 12 weeks in length.

## University of Houston—College of Technology

*Diesel Technology*

| First Semester | Credit | Second Semester | Credit |
|---|---|---|---|
| Diesel Theory | 6 | Diesel Shop | 6 |
| Memos, Report, and Letters | 3 | Electricity: Direct Current | 4 |
| Industrial Drafting Fundamentals | 3 | Blueprint Reading | 3 |
| Specialized Machine Shop | 3 | Elementary Physics | 3 |
| Basic Technical Math | 3 | Advanced Technical Math | 3 |
| | 18 | | 19 |

| Third Semester | | Fourth Semester | |
|---|---|---|---|
| Electricity: Alt. Current | 4 | Power Plant Design | 3 |
| Business Organization | 3 | Mechanical Power Transmission | 3 |
| Industrial Mechanics | 3 | Advanced Theory and Design | 4 |
| Strength of Materials | 3 | Employer-Employee Relations | 3 |
| Thermodynamics | 3 | Approved Electives | 3 |
| | 16 | | 16 |

## Wentworth Institute

*Industrial Electronics*

First Year

| First Semester | Credit | Second Semester | Credit |
|---|---|---|---|
| Electric Circuits | 4 | Electric Circuits | 5 |
| Electron Tubes and Circuits | 4 | Electron Tubes and Circuits | 5 |
| Algebra and Trigonometry | 4 | Algebra and Trigonometry | 4 |
| Physics: Mechanics | 4 | Physics: Heat, Sound, and Light | 4 |
| English Composition | 3 | Electronic Drafting | 1 |
| Mechanical Drawing | 2 | Shop Techniques | 1 |
| Shop Techniques | 1 | | |
| | 22 | | 20 |

Second Year

| First Semester | Credit | Second Semester | Credit |
|---|---|---|---|
| Electron Tubes and Circuits | 6 | Electron Tubes and Circuits | 4 |
| Special Tubes and Circuits | 6 | Special Tubes and Circuits | 5 |
| Introduction to Calculus | 3 | Analytic Geometry and Mathematical Analysis | 3 |
| Electronic Drafting | 1 | Oral Communication | 2 |
| Electrical Machinery Measurements | 2 | Electrical Machinery Measurements | 5 |
| Electrical Machinery Lab | 2 | Wiring Practice | 1 |
| Shop Techniques | 1 | Shop Techniques | 1 |
| | 21 | | 21 |

## Appendix 6. In-service course[1]

*Topic I. The Technical Institute as a Community College in New York City*

Session 1. Origin: Background, need and purpose, legislation.

*Topic II. Technical Institute and Community College Instruction*

Session 2. Methods of instruction found best in various curriculums; improvement of instruction; and integration of instruction.

*Topic III. Technical Institute Staff and Plant*

Session 3. Personnel: Staff, students, trustees, advisory commissions.

Session 4. Physical Organization: Plant, equipment, finance.

*Topic IV. Differences between Community College in New York City and Other Higher Education*

Session 5. Differences in objectives, sponsorship, community responsibilities, faculty, student body, curriculum, physical plant, working conditions, and financing.

*Topic V. Administrative Organization*

Session 6. Role of State University, City of New York, Board of Trustees, the Director, administrative officers, faculty; Faculty Senate and Faculty Committee; nonteaching staff—clerical and maintenance.

[1] This course was offered to all faculty members of the New York City Community College of Applied Arts and Sciences in the fall of 1952.

*Topic VI. Financing Technical Institute and Community College*

Session 7. Budget: Source of money; how spent; limitations; relationship to personnel, curriculum, physical plant.

*Topic VII. Development of New Community College Programs*

Session 8. Evidence available in complete studies (Cottrel Report); experience of the Institute; methods and techniques of development of new programs; faculty participation; relationship of General Education to Community College education; opportunities for faculty.

*Topic VIII. Adult Education and Community Extension Service*

Session 9. Need for adult education, origins of Extension Division, staff, students, financing additional services.

*Topic IX. Recent Legislative Development in Community College Education*

## Appendix 7. Freshman questionnaire

Rochester Institute of Technology, Rochester,
New York, Fall, 1954

Department________________

To the entering Freshman:

We are happy to have you at the Institute and trust that your stay here will be an enjoyable and profitable one. It is because you are new here that we are coming to you for information. Many impressions are still fresh in your mind and we should like to have your reactions to the following questions in order that we may do an even better job with other freshman classes which will follow. Will you, therefore, kindly answer the questions carefully and thoughtfully? We are not asking you to sign your name and should like you to be perfectly frank.

MARK ELLINGSON, PRESIDENT

1. Through which of the following did you first hear about R.I.T.? (Please check *one*)
   __A graduate or former student
   __A present student at R.I.T.
   __R.I.T. instructor or staff member
   __R.I.T. representative who visited my school
   __High school principal
   __High school guidance counselor
   __High school teacher
   __A friend

__A relative
__Newspaper article
__Poster
__Radio or television
__R.I.T. catalogue
__Other R.I.T. publications
__Other (Please explain)________________________

2. Location of high school from which you graduated. (Please check)
__Rochester
__Monroe County (other than Rochester)
__New York State (other than Rochester or Monroe County)
__Out of state

3. Do you believe that the average high school student obtains enough information about R.I.T.? Yes__ No__ If "No," what might be done to let prospective students and others know more about the Institute?____________

4. What factors, persons, or events do you believe were most important in influencing you to come to R.I.T.? (Check three items by placing a "1" in the blank opposite the most important item, and a "2" and a "3" opposite the second and third most important factors.)
__My parents
__Relatives other than my parents
__A graduate of R.I.T. or former student
__A present student at R.I.T.
__My high school principal

__My high school guidance counselor
__One of my high school teachers (If so, teacher's field ______)
__R.I.T. representative who visited my school
__Personal interview at R.I.T.
__R.I.T. publications mailed to me
__R.I.T. Open House or visit to Institute
__Suggestion of R.I.T. Counseling Center
__Reputation of R.I.T. in my field of interest
__Physical plant of R.I.T. (Shops, labs, etc.)
__R.I.T. now offers the Bachelor of Science degree
__More practical type of education than offered in other colleges
__Dormitory facilities and program
__Sports or other extracurricular activities
__Co-op work program will give me a chance to earn part of my way
__Could live at home and commute
__Other reasons (Please explain)____________________

5. Are either one or both of your parents graduates of R.I.T.? Yes__ No__

6. Did any of your high school teachers or counselors encourage you to attend R.I.T.? Yes__ No__

   Did any of your high school teachers or counselors discourage you from attending R.I.T.? Yes__ No__ If the answer to this question is "Yes," what was the chief reason for discouraging you?____________________

7. Before you actually registered at R.I.T., what were the things you liked about your contacts with the Institute, either in person or by mail?____________________

   What were the things you did not like, or which you believe might be improved?____________________

8. What are the things that you have liked about the Institute methods of helping a freshman get acquainted with the school, with other students, and with the faculty?____

   What were the things you did not like, which you believe might be improved?____________________

9. Are there any other suggestions or comments you care to make which would help us to improve the Institute?____

10. Where did you rank in your high school graduating class? (Example: ranked 5 in a class of 100.)________________

## Appendix 8. Questionnaire on teaching effectiveness

Rochester Institute of Technology, Rochester, New York

Department__________ Name of Course__________
Block and Section__________ Name of Instructor__________

To the Student: On this blank we should like to have you give your honest opinion regarding various aspects of this course. The answers which you give will be held in strict confidence and the results will be compiled by the Educational Research Office.

Place a check mark in the proper space to indicate your opinion of each item.

| | Unsatisfactory | Satisfactory | Average | Good | Excellent |
|---|---|---|---|---|---|
| 1. Instructor's knowledge of the subject. . . . . . . . . . . . | | | | | |
| 2. Clarity and thoroughness of presentation. . . . . . . . . | | | | | |
| 3. Ability to hold class interest and stimulate thinking | | | | | |
| 4. Interest in students and willingness to be of assistance. . . . . . . . . . . . . . . . . | | | | | |
| 5. Open-mindedness, willingness to present both sides of a question. . . . . . . . . . | | | | | |
| 6. Fairness of grading on tests and assigned work. . | | | | | |
| 7. Correlation of lectures, text, lab work, and quizzes | | | | | |
| 8. Personal appearance and poise. . . . . . . . . . . . . . . . . | | | | | |
| 9. Considering everything, rate this instructor's general teaching effectiveness | | | | | |

To the Student: In the questions which follow we should like to have you give any suggestions which you believe would be of assistance to this instructor and to the Institute.

10. What were the strongest or best aspects of this course as far as you were concerned?____________________

11. What were the weakest or poorest aspects of this course?
________________________________________

12. What specific suggestions would you make that might be of assistance to this instructor in improving his teaching effectiveness?____________________________

13. Do you have any other specific suggestions which you believe would be of assistance to your department head or to the administrative officers of the Institute in improving the total program?__________________________

## Appendix 9. Representative organizational charts of technical institutes

Off-campus Centers of the Pennsylvania State University are located in each of eleven geographical areas into which the State is divided for maximum coverage. The large variety of educational services offered makes the centers community colleges in the true sense. Each of these services draws from the resources available on the main campus of the University.

The two-year full-time technical institute associate degree programs are one of the important services offered in ten of the eleven centers. Drafting and design technology and electrical technology comprise the curriculums now being offered, with the additional curriculum of metals technology (metallurgy) scheduled to be added in September, 1955.

In administrative matters the centers are under the supervision of the Director of General Extension, whose place in the university organization is shown in Chart 1. The College of Engineering and Architecture, which is also shown in Chart 1, supervises the centers in respect to educational matters. These administrative relationships between the centers and their central headquarters are shown in more detail in Chart 2 and Chart 3. The technical institute programs is operated and administered within the organization of the center, as set forth in Chart 4.

All matters pertaining to operation, administration, and development flow through the general extension administration organization as shown on Chart 3. All matters pertaining to the academic phases of the program follow through the various colleges of the University as shown, for example, on Chart 2. Curriculums now being offered, namely, drafting and design technology and electrical technology, are under the academic jurisdiction of the College of Engineering and Architecture. Metals technology is under the academic jurisdiction of the College of Mineral Industries.

Each college has an extension department headed by a director who reports directly to the dean of his college on matters pertaining to extension work. The extension directors of all colleges, in turn, make up the Council on Extension (Chart 3), which is advisory to the Director of General Extension. Liaison is also established between the directors of the various extension divisions of the colleges and the general extension administration divisions shown on Chart 4.

A study of Charts 1 to 4 shows a direct-line organization from the president's office down through the general extension administration division for the operation and administration of a center and through the respective colleges (see example, Chart 2, College of Engineering and Architecture) that exercise academic jurisdiction over the program.

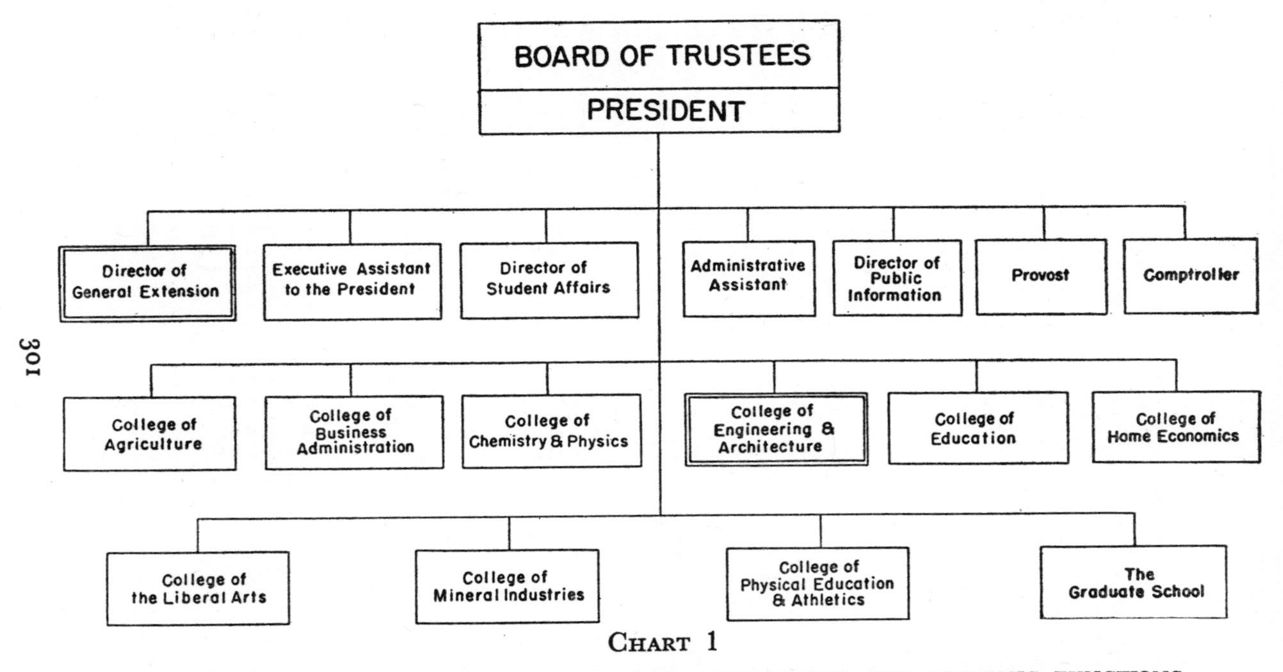


CHART 1

PENNSYLVANIA STATE UNIVERSITY—BASIC ADMINISTRATIVE AND ACADEMIC FUNCTIONS

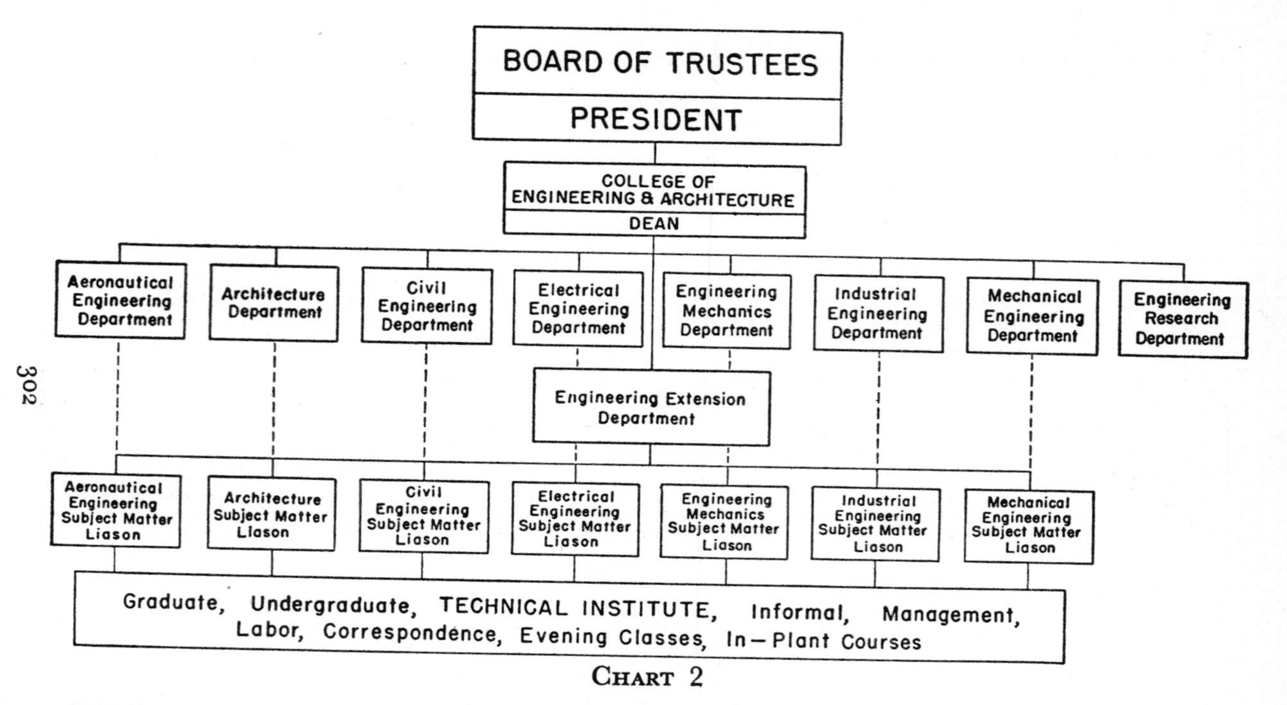


CHART 2

PENNSYLVANIA STATE UNIVERSITY—RELATION OF SUBJECT MATTER IN TECHNICAL INSTITUTES TO DEPARTMENTS

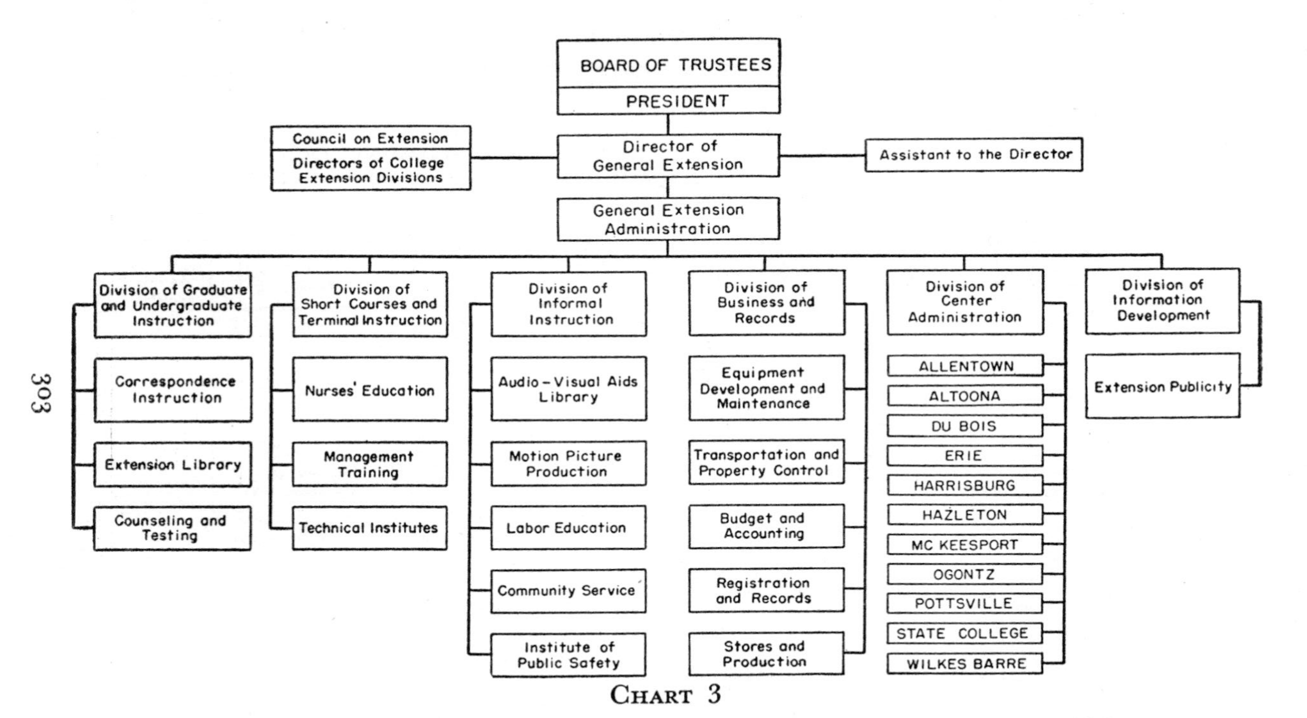


CHART 3

PENNSYLVANIA STATE UNIVERSITY—GENERAL EXTENSION ADMINISTRATION

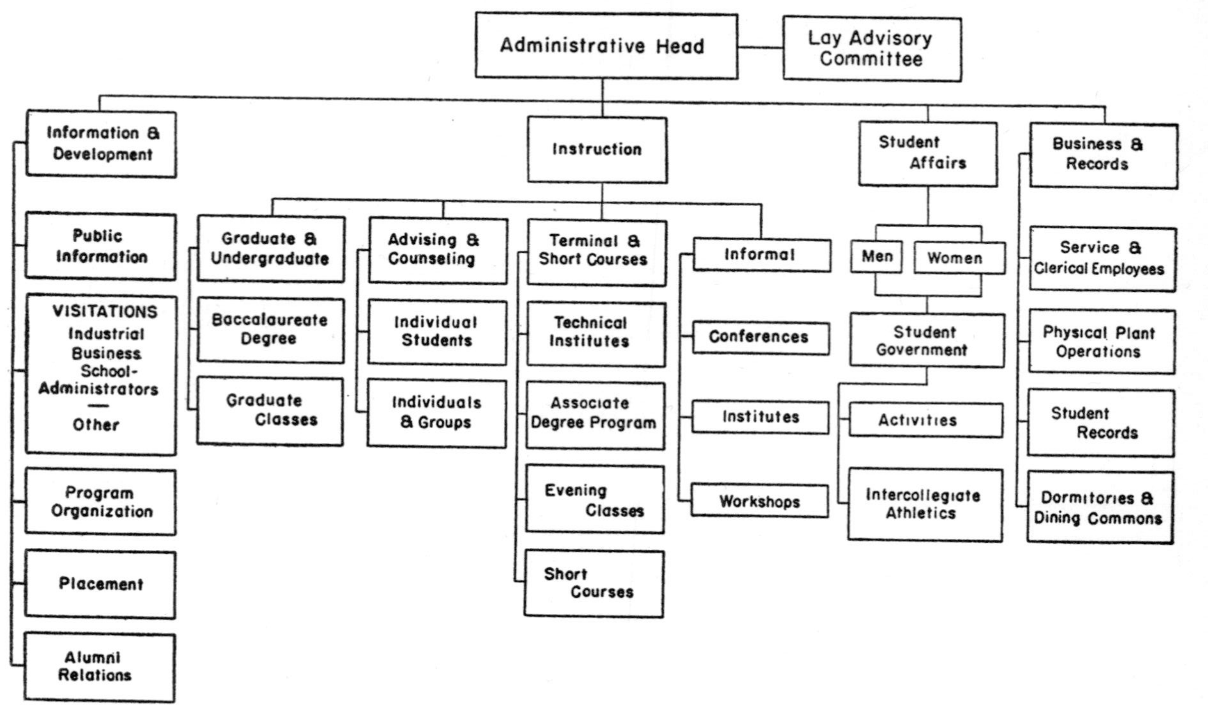


CHART 4

PENNSYLVANIA STATE UNIVERSITY—ORGANIZATION OF OFF-CAMPUS CENTERS

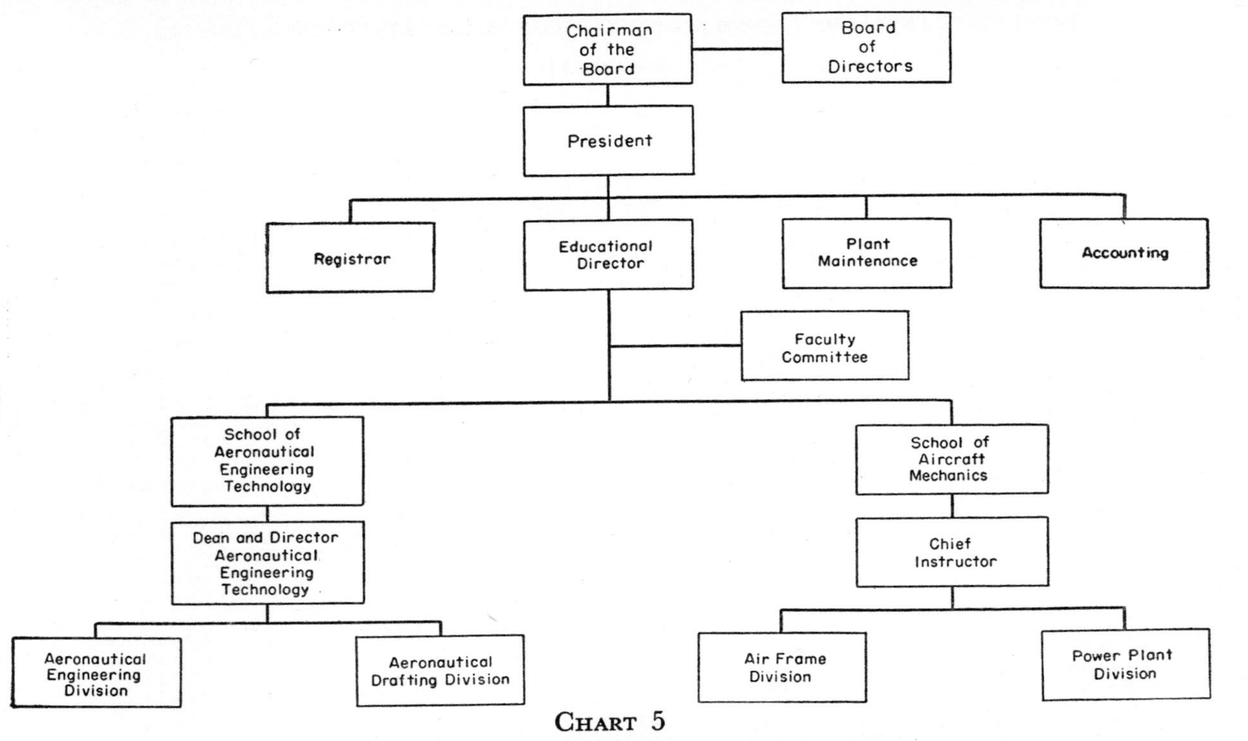


CHART 5

ORGANIZATION OF AERONAUTICAL UNIVERSITY

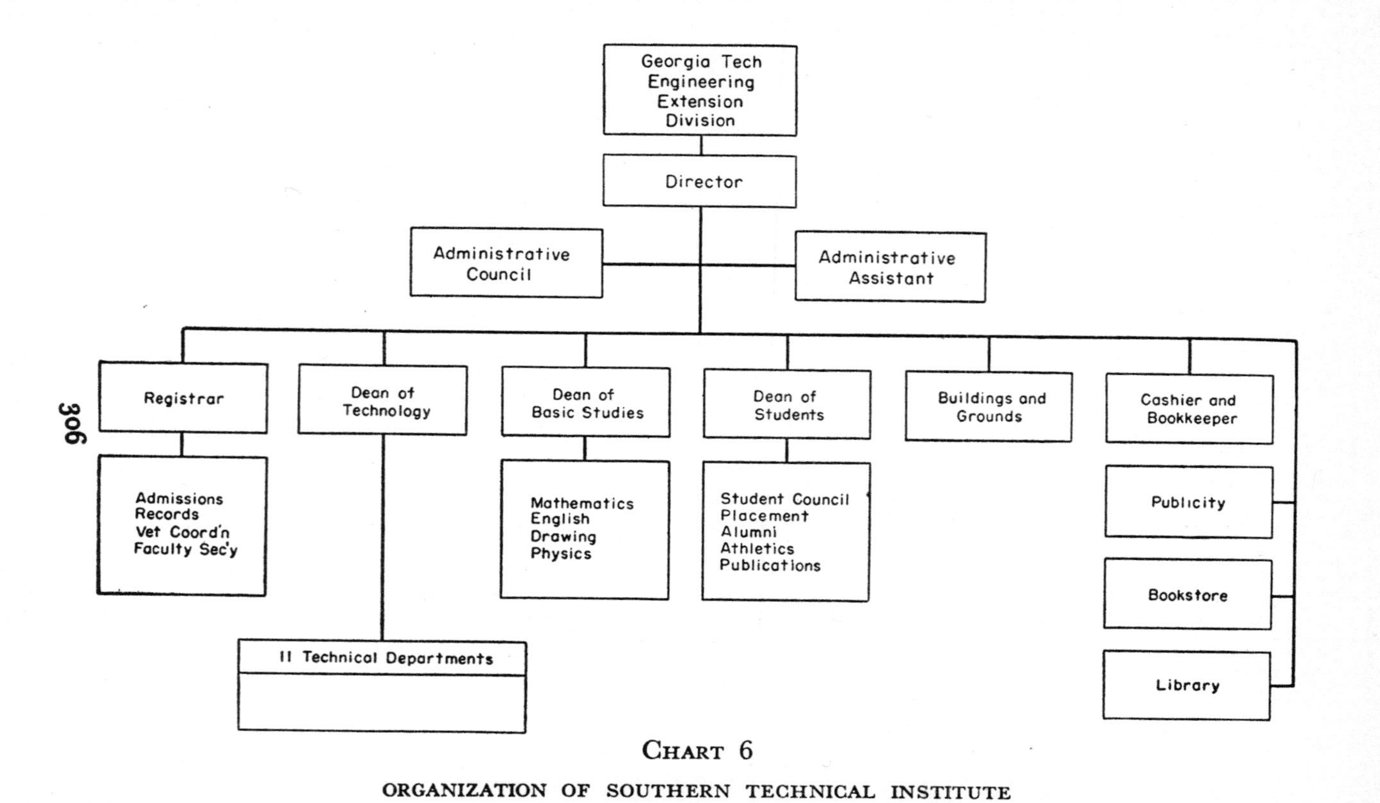


CHART 6

ORGANIZATION OF SOUTHERN TECHNICAL INSTITUTE

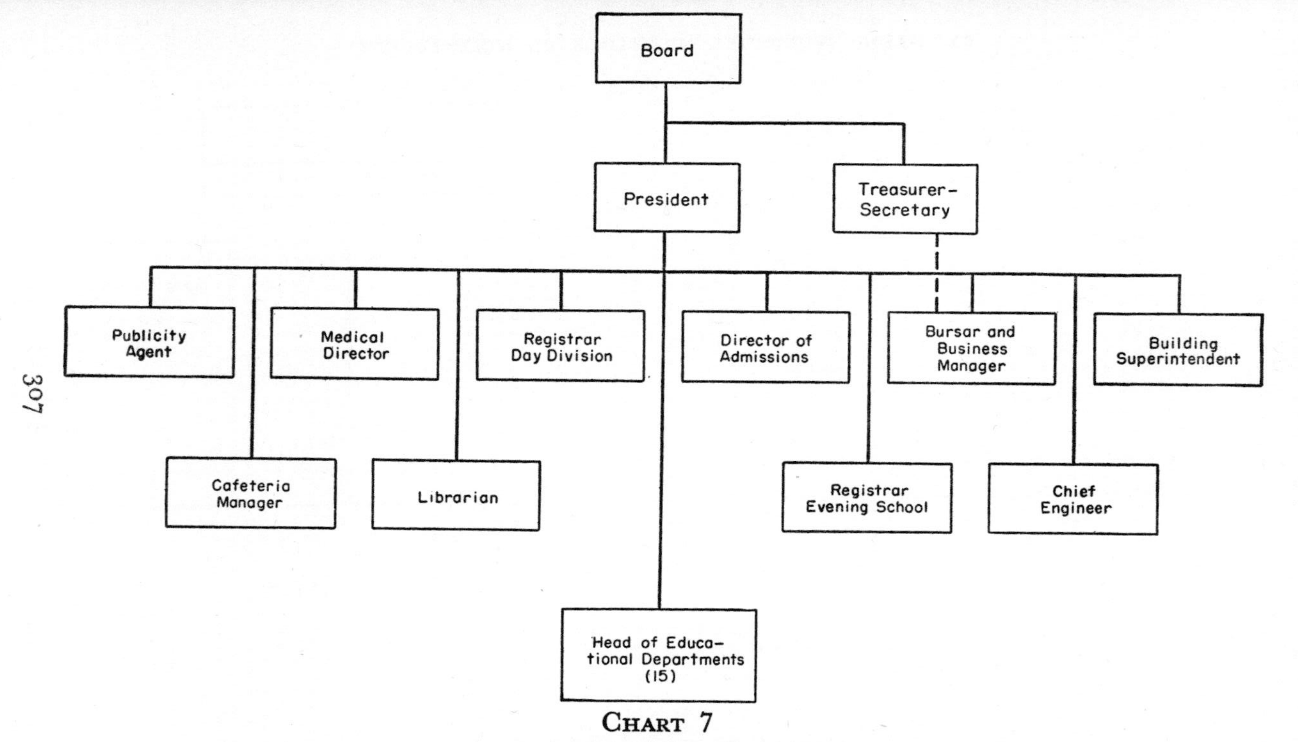


CHART 7

ORGANIZATION OF WENTWORTH INSTITUTE

# Index

Academy of Aeronautics, 11, 52, 249–250, 265, 274, 282
Accredited curriculums, 6–7, 12–13, 32, 249–262
*Accrediting, Revised Manual of,* 223*n.*, 226*n.*
Acme School of Die Design Engineering, 52, 265, 274
Activity analysis, 132
  and curriculum content, 134
  Rochester Institute of Technology, 135–136
Adams, H. P., 27
Administration, 222–243
  budget, 230–231
  business, 229–231
  evaluation, 238–241
  financing, 227–231
  instructional program, 234–235
  organizational structure, 225–227, 299–307
  plant, 231
  principles of, 236, 242–243
  student personnel, 235–236
Admissions, 172–177, 181–182
  interviews, 176–177
  requirements, 174
  tests, 174–176
Aeronautical technology, 58, 64, 70, 249–250, 255, 268, 272, 274, 282
Aeronautical University, 52, 265, 274, 305
Agricultural curriculums, 62, 66, 72, 276
Air-conditioning and heating curriculums, 58, 64, 70, 252, 254, 256, 259, 268, 270, 272, 274
Aircraft curriculums, 58, 64, 70, 249–250, 255, 268, 270, 272, 274, 282
Aircraft-design curriculums, 58, 64, 70, 249, 268, 282
Alliance Technical Institute, 50, 82, 228, 264, 270
Almstead, Francis E., 142*n.*
American Association of Junior Colleges, study on terminal education, 29, 45, 205
American Council on Education, 140
American Society for Engineering Education, Technical Institute Division, 33–34, 69
American Television Institute of Technology, 52, 266, 274

Andrews, Frank E., 228*n.*
Apparel technology curriculum, 62, 66, 72, 277
Applied art curriculums, 68, 72, 76, 277–279
Arbuckle, Dugald S., 181*n.*
Architectural curriculums, 58, 64, 70, 252, 253, 255–257, 259, 261, 268, 270, 272, 274, 288
Armsby, Henry H., 57*n.*, 68*n.*, 205*n.*, 208*n.*, 211*n.*
Art curriculums, 62, 66, 72, 277, 279
Automotive and diesel technology curriculums, 58, 64, 70, 268, 270, 272

Beach, Kenneth, 124*n.*
Beese, C. W., 5*n.*, 9*n.*, 35
Berdie, Ralph, 188*n.*
Bliss Electrical School, 24
Bogue, Jesse P., 30, 44, 225*n.*
Booher, Edward E., 14*n.*, 15*n.*, 30, 32, 78, 144
Bowen, H. A., 199*n.*
Bowman Technical School, 52, 266, 274
Boykin, L. L., 199*n.*
Bradley Polytechnic Institute, 27
Brayfield, Arthur H., 188*n.*
Brooklyn Polytechnic Institute, 27
Broome County Technical Institute, 48, 208, 211, 263, 268, 276, 283
Brouwer, Paul J., 181*n.*
Budget, 230–231
Building construction curriculums, 66, 70, 74, 252, 253, 255–257, 259, 261, 268, 270, 272, 274, 288
Business curriculums, 62, 66, 277

Cal-Aero Technical Institute, 52, 266
California State Polytechnic College, 48, 263, 276
*Call for Action, A*, American Council on Education, 37*n.*
Canadian technical institutes, 41, 44, 47, 55, 266–267
Capitol Radio Engineering Institute, 11, 52, 250, 266, 274
Carnegie Institute of Technology, 27
Census of distribution of labor force, 114–115
Central Technical Institute, 11, 52, 251, 266, 274, 278, 284
Chambers, R. F., 199*n.*
Charters, W. W., 104, 109*n.*
Chemistry curriculums, 58, 64, 70, 251, 258, 268, 270, 272
Chicago Technical College, 52, 266, 274
Cincinnati, Univeristy of, 204, 205
Civil technology curriculums, 58, 64, 70, 259, 268, 272, 274
Clarkson College of Technology, 27
Clothing and textile curriculums, 63, 67, 73, 277, 279
Cogswell Polytechnical College, 50, 251, 264, 270

College of William and Mary, 51, 272
Colvert, C. C., 45
Connecticut State Technical Institute, 48, 263, 268
Cooper Union, 27
Cooperative education, 203–221
  administration of, 212
  coordination of, 215–216, 219–221
  curriculums, 211
  enrollment in cooperative programs, 208
  history of, 204
  job circuit, 217
  reports from employers, 219
  reports from students, 219
Cooperative work, 196, 203–221
Counseling, 187–191
Cowen, Philip A., 96
Credentials, need for, 92
Curriculum, 129–146
  construction of, 130–132
    from activity analysis, 134–139
    general principles, 145–146
    from job charts, 132–134
Curriculums, components of, 69, 74–78
  enrollment in (*see* Enrollment)
  general education, 76
  nontechnological, 62–63
  representative, 282–290
  technological, 58–59
  types of, 57, 60
  typical, 144

Das, Radha C., 76
Davis, Warren, 140, 142
Dayton, University of, 51, 260, 265, 272
Degree, associate, 32, 34
Dental hygiene curriculum, 63, 67, 73, 277
Dental laboratory technology curriculum, 63, 67, 73, 277
Detroit Engineering Institute, 52, 274
*Dictionary of Occupational Titles*, 121
Diesel curriculums, 59, 65, 71, 252, 254, 256, 268, 289
Dobbs, Frederick E., 23, 36
Drafting curriculums, 59, 65, 71, 256, 257, 269, 271, 273, 275
Drexel Institute of Technology, 27
Drop-outs, 124
Dyrness, Enock C., 242*n.*

Ecole Provinciale de Papeterie, 55, 266
ECPD (*see* Engineers' Council for Professional Development)
Eells, Walter C., 28*n.*, 29*n.*, 45
Electrical technology curriculums, 66, 70, 74, 252–262, 269, 271, 273, 284, 286, 287
Electronics curriculums, 52, 59, 64, 71, 251, 253, 259–261, 266, 269, 271, 273, 274, 284, 290
Electronics Institute, Inc., 52, 266, 274
Ell, Carl S., 215*n.*
Ellingson, Mark, 134*n.*, 136, 138*n.*, 156, 240*n.*

Embry Riddle International School of Aviation, 266
Emerson, Lynn A., 134
*Employment Outlook for Technicians,* 167*n.*
*Engineering Technician, The,* 167*n.*
Engineers' Council for Professional Development, accreditation of technical institutes, 6–7, 12–13, 32
  accredited curriculums, 6–7, 12–13, 32, 249*n.*
  subcommittee on technical institutes, 32
Enrollment, 38–55, 60–61, 64–67
  Canadian institutes, 55
  extension divisions of colleges and universities, 51
  privately endowed institutes, 50
  proprietary institutes, 52–53
  state and municipal institutes, 48–49
  total in technical institutes, 47, 64–67
  YMCA schools, 54
Erie County Technical Institute, 48, 208, 211, 263, 268, 276
Evaluation, 240
Extension divisions of colleges and universities, 41, 43, 47, 51, 58–59, 62–73, 265, 272–273, 278–279

Fashion Institute of Technology, 48, 263, 268, 276
Fenn College, 11, 51, 265
Financial aids, 195–197
Fire protection technology curriculum, 59, 65, 71, 256, 269, 273, 285
Food administration curriculums, 63, 67, 73, 277, 279
Food processing technology curriculum, 59, 65, 71, 269
Food service, 183–184
Foster, C. L., 78*n.*
Franklin Technical Institute, 11, 23, 50, 251, 270, 278
Franklin University Technical Institute, 54, 252, 264, 266, 270
Freshman questionnaire, 293–296
Freund, C. J., 206*n.*

Gamble, Charles W., 228*n.*
Gardiner (Maine) Lyceum, 20
Gas fuel technology curriculum, 59, 65, 71, 259, 269, 273
General education, 76, 107, 139, 142–144
*General Education in a Free Society,* 139*n.*
General Motors Institute, 208, 211, 218
Georgia Institute of Technology, 11, 27
Goetsch, Walter R., 224*n.*
Graduates, 80–100
  Alliance Technical Institute, 82
  Community College and Technical Institute of Temple University, 88
  initial job placements, 83
  job progress, 93
  job titles, 94

Graduates, Long Island Agricultural and Technical Institute, 83
Milwaukee School of Engineering, 90
numbers of, 61, 68, 69, 70–73
Oregon Technical Institute, 82
Pennsylvania State University Technical Institutes, 85–87
Purdue University Technical Institutes, 86, 88
Rochester Institute of Technology, 84
salary trends, 94–95
transfer problems, 94
types of positions held, 80, 82–88, 90
Graney, Maurice R., 156*n.*
Graphic arts curriculums, 62, 66, 72
Guidance materials, 167–168

Hagberg, Sherman, 135*n.*
Hammond, H. P., 32, 35, 69*n.*
Hammond, Kenneth, 69*n.*, 75*n.*, 77*n.*
Hampton, Thomas E., 116*n.*, 120*n.*
Harper, Arthur, 36
Health curriculums, 63, 67, 73
Health services, 185–187
Hillyer College, Ward School of Electronics, 51, 272
Hoke, George W., 23*n.*
Holderman, K. L., 148, 160*n.*
Hollis, Ernest V., 228*n.*
Home economics curriculums, 63, 67, 73
Hotel technology curriculums, 62, 66, 72, 277
Housing, 183–184
Houston, University of, College of Technology, 11, 27, 51, 252, 265, 272, 289
Hudson Valley Technical Institute, 48, 263, 268

Illinois Institute of Technology, 27
Indianapolis Electronic School, 52, 266, 274
Industrial electronics, 52, 59, 64, 71, 251, 253, 260, 261, 269, 271, 273, 274, 284, 290
Industrial technology curriculums, 59, 65, 71, 253, 259, 260, 269, 271, 273, 275
Industrial Trades Institute, 52, 266
Instruction methods, 159–160
Instructors, 147–161
education, 149–150
experience, 147–149
qualifications, 147–151
recruitment, 150–153
teaching effectiveness, 297–298
teaching loads, 160–161
training, 156–158, 291–292
Instrumentation curriculums, 59, 64, 71, 269, 273

James H. McGraw Award, 32, 35
Jaracz, W. A., 68*n.*
Jarvie, Lawrence L., 153*n.*, 158, 240*n.*
Job chart, 91
Job cluster, 132
Johnson, L. V., 110, 111*n.*
Johnson, N. A., 199*n.*

Junior college, role of, 28–31
terminal education in, 29, 44, 45, 205

Kirkpatrick, F. H., 199*n.*
Klitgord, Otto, 158*n.*, 161*n.*
Kolbe, Park R., 215*n.*

Lain Drafting College, 52, 253, 266, 274
Lakehead Technical Institute, 55, 266
Lawrence Institute of Technology, 51, 265
Le Tourneau Technical Institute, 50, 264, 270, 278
Lipsett, Laurence, 99*n.*, 164*n.*
*Literature Significant to Education of the Technical Institute Type: An Annotated Bibliography*, 34*n.*
Lloyd-Jones, Esther, 181*n.*
Long Island Agricultural and Technical Institute, 48, 81, 83, 92, 170, 263, 268, 276
Los Angeles City College, 12
Lowell Institute School, 51, 265

McGrath, Dorothy L., 140*n.*
McGraw-Hill award, 32, 35
McGraw-Hill textbook contest, 160
Machine shop curriculums, 59, 65, 71, 269, 271, 273
Maritime academies, 42
Marsh, R. Warren, 94
Master, Carmine, 69*n.*, 75*n.*, 77*n.*
Mechanical technology curriculums, 59, 65, 71, 251, 252, 254, 255, 257, 258, 260, 261, 269, 271, 273, 283
Mechanics Institute, New York City, 19*n.*, 50, 264
Medden, Mary, 184*n.*
Medical laboratory technology curriculums, 63, 67, 73, 277
Medical office assisting curriculums, 63, 67, 73
Medical services, 185–187
Metallurgical technology curriculums, 59, 65, 71, 271, 273
Milwaukee School of Engineering, 24–25, 50, 90, 253, 264, 270
Mohawk Valley Technical Institute, 48, 263, 268, 276
Montgomery Junior College, 24
Montreal Technical School, 55, 267
Morrill Act, 26
Morrison, J. Cayce, 14*n.*, 106*n.*, 116*n.*, 125, 132*n.*, 141*n.*
Multnomah College, 50, 270

National Council of Technical Schools, 6, 33, 168*n.*
National Technical Institute, 266
New Bedford Institute of Textiles, 48, 263, 268
New England Technical Institute, 53, 266, 274
New Hampshire Technical Institute, 157
Manchester, 48, 263, 268, 276
Portsmouth, 48, 263, 268

New Haven YMCA Junior College, 12
New York City Community College, 48, 157, 170, 208, 211, 263, 268, 276
New York State Agricultural and Technical Institute, Alfred, 48, 254, 264, 268, 276
  Canton, 48, 254–255, 264, 268, 276
  Delhi, 49, 264, 268, 276
  Morrisville, 49, 106, 264, 268, 276
New York State Committee on Curriculums, 132, 141
New York State Institute of Agriculture and Home Economics, Cobleskill, 49, 264, 276
New York State Institutes of Applied Arts and Sciences, 40, 78, 209
New York State School of Labor and Industrial Relations, 157
New York State technical institutes, 96, 106
New York University, 265
North Dakota State School of Science, 49, 264, 268, 276
Northeastern University, 218
Northrop Aeronautical Institute, 11, 53, 255, 266, 274

Objectives, 103–112
  building program from, 111–112
  definition of, 104
  Rochester Institute of Technology, 110
  steps in preparing, 108
Ohio Mechanics Institute, 10, 11, 19–22, 31, 50, 208, 209, 211, 255, 264, 270
Oklahoma Agricultural and Mechanical College, 11, 27, 51, 106, 256, 265, 272, 285
Oklahoma Institute of Technology, 155
Optical technology curriculum, 59, 65, 71, 269
Oregon Technical Institute, 49, 82, 256, 264, 268, 276
Organizational charts, 226, 299–307
  Aeronautical University, 305
  Pennsylvania State University, 299–304
  Southern Technical Institute, 306
  Wentworth Institute, 307
Orientation, 182–183

Park, Clyde W., 204*n.*
Pasadena Junior College, 12
Penn Technical Institute, 53, 266, 274
Pennsylvania State University Technical Institutes, 11, 27, 40, 51, 85–87, 171, 257, 265, 272, 278, 286, 299–304
Perry, Walter S., 22*n.*
Philadelphia Wireless Technical Institute, 50, 264, 270
Philco Corporation, 260
Photography curriculums, 62, 66, 72, 258, 279
Placement, 197–200
  (*See also* Graduates)
Plant, 231–233

Practical nursing curriculums, 63, 67, 73, 277, 279
Pratt Institute, 22, 27
Printing and publishing curriculums, 62, 66, 72, 277, 279
Privately endowed technical institutes, 41, 43, 47, 50, 58–59, 264–265, 270–271, 278–279
Proprietary technical institutes, 41, 43, 47, 52–53, 58–59, 64–65, 70–71, 265–266, 274–275, 278–279
Provincial Institute of Mining, 55, 267
Provincial Institute of Technology and Art, 55, 267
Provincial Institute of Textiles, 55, 267
Public relations, 237
Publicity, 169
Publishing and printing curriculums, 62, 66, 72, 277, 279
Purdue University, Division of Technical Institutes, 11, 27, 40, 51, 86, 88, 156, 257, 265, 272, 278, 287
Putnam Technical School, 49, 264, 268

Radio and television curriculums, 59, 64, 71, 250–253, 256, 258, 259, 261, 269, 271, 273, 275, 284, 287
Radio Television Institute, Inc., 266
RCA Institutes, Inc., 11, 53, 116, 258, 266, 274
Reck, W. Emerson, 170*n.*, 237*n.*
Recruitment of students, 163–172, 293–296
Reed, Anna Y., 181*n.*
Reeves, Floyd W., 223*n.*, 230*n.*
Refrigeration curriculums, 58, 64, 70, 252, 254
Reilly, William J., 188*n.*
Remedial services, 191–193
Rensselaer Polytechnic Institute, 26
Retail distribution curriculums, 62, 66, 72, 277, 279
Rochester Athenaeum and Mechanics Institute, 23
(*See also* Rochester Institute of Technology)
Rochester Institute of Technology, 11, 22, 50, 84, 91, 96, 98, 107, 116, 156, 164, 204, 207, 208, 211, 217, 240, 258, 264, 270, 278
objectives, 110
photographic technology curriculum, 106
screw machine technology curriculum, 106
Rodes, Harold P., 45
Rogers, Carl R., 188*n.*
Rose Polytechnic Institute, 27
Russell, John Dale, 181*n.*, 223*n.*, 230*n.*
Ryerson Institute of Technology, 55, 267

Salary trends, 94–95
Sales, industrial, curriculums, 62, 66, 72, 277

Saxby, Orvis H., 23*n.*
Schneider, Herman, 204
Scholarships and loans, 195–196
School of Industrial Arts, 49, 264
Secretarial curriculums, 68, 72, 76, 277, 279
Sharpe, Russell T., 197*n.*
Sheet-metal curriculums, 59, 65, 71, 269
Sinclair College, 54, 266, 270, 278
Smith, Leo F., 13*n.*, 38*n.*, 47*n.*, 50*n.*, 51*n.*, 57*n.*, 99*n.*, 124*n.*, 164*n.*, 203*n.*, 205*n.*, 213*n.*
Smith, Margaret R., 197*n.*
Society for the Promotion of Engineering Education, *A Study of Technical Institutes,* 4, 25, 38, 129, 148, 149, 206
Southern Illinois University, 51, 272, 278
Southern Technical Institute, 27, 51, 106, 259, 265, 272, 288, 306
Spahr, Robert H., 4, 6, 13*n.*, 20*n.*, 25*n.*, 26*n.*, 29*n.*, 35, 38*n.*, 95*n.*, 129*n.*, 148*n.*, 153*n.*, 159*n.*, 206*n.*
Spartan School of Aeronautics, 53, 266, 274
SPEE (*see* Society for the Promotion of Engineering Education)
Spring Garden Institute, 23, 50, 260, 264, 270, 278
State and municipal technical institutes, 41–43, 47–49, 58–59, 263–264, 268, 269, 276–277
Stationary engineering curriculum, 252
Steam and diesel technology curriculums, 59, 65, 71, 262, 271, 273
Story, Robert C., 57*n.*
Strang, Ruth, 182, 200*n.*
Stratton, Burton E., 195*n.*
Structural technology curriculums, 58, 64, 70, 252, 268, 270
*Student Personnel Point of View, The,* 181*n.*
*Student Personnel Programs in Transition,* 181*n.*
Student personnel records, 200–201
Student personnel services, 179–202
  types of, 180
Students, activities of, 193–195
  recruitment of, 163–172, 293–296
  (*See also* Enrollment)
*Study of Technical Institutes, A,* 4, 25, 38, 129, 148, 149, 206
Surveying technology, 257
Surveys, Annual Survey of Technical Institutes, 42, 57
  interviews, 120–122
  methods, 113–128
  on need for technical institute education, 13–15
  questionnaires, 120

Teaching effectiveness, questionnaire on, 297–298
*Technical Education News,* 33, 34, 38
Technical institute education, need for, 13–15
  significant developments in, 31–36

"Technical Institute Profiles," Bliss Electrical School, 24*n.*
Milwaukee School of Engineering, 24*n.*
Wyomissing Polytechnic Institute, 209*n.*
*Technical Institute Programs in the United States,* ECPD, 7*n.*
Technical institutes, bibliography on, 34
Canadian, 41, 44, 47, 55
definition of, 3
extension divisions of colleges and universities, 41, 43, 47, 51
privately endowed, 41, 43, 47, 50
proprietary, 41, 43, 47, 52–53
specific objectives of, 105–107
state and municipal, 41–43, 47–49
types of, 10–13
YMCA schools, 41, 44, 47, 54
Technical jobs, criteria of, 117, 280–281
TechRep Division, Philco Corporation, 260
Television technology curriculums, 67, 70, 75, 250–253, 258, 269, 271, 273, 275, 284, 287
Temple University, Community College and Technical Institute, 51, 88–89, 265, 272
Textile design curriculums, 62, 66, 72, 277
Textile technology curriculums, 59, 65, 71, 269
Thompson, Florence M., 184*n.*
Tool- and die-making and design curriculums, 59, 65, 71, 253, 262, 269, 271, 273, 275
Tyler, Ralph W., 238*n.*

Valparaiso Technical Institute, 53, 261, 266, 274
Van Zeeland, Fred J., 151*n.*
*Vocational-Technical Training for Industrial Occupations,* 14*n.*, 15, 118*n.*, 120*n.*, 122*n.*, 134*n.*

*Wanted: 30,000 Instructors,* American Council on Education, 147*n.*, 151*n.*, 154*n.*, 156*n.*, 161*n.*
Ward, Phebe, 29*n.*, 123
Ward School of Electronics, 51
Watch and jewelry technology curriculums, 59, 65, 71, 269, 275
Weber College, 116
Welding technology curriculums, 59, 65, 71, 254, 269, 271, 273, 275
Wentworth Institute, 11, 23, 50, 261, 265, 270, 290, 307
Werwath, Karl, 24
Werwath, Oscar, 24
West Virginia Institute of Technology, 51, 262, 272, 278
Westchester Community College, 49, 208, 211, 264, 268, 276
Wickenden, W. E., 4, 6, 13*n.*, 20*n.*, 25*n.*, 26*n.*, 29*n.*, 38*n.*, 95*n.*, 129*n.*, 148*n.*, 153*n.*, 159*n.*, 206*n.*

William and Mary, College of, 265, 272
Williams, Paul M., 96–97
Williamson, E. G., 181*n.*
Williston, Arthur L., 23, 26, 35
Wrenn, C. Gilbert, 179*n.*, 180*n.*, 184*n.*, 187*n.*, 188*n.*, 197*n.*, 201*n.*
Wyomissing Polytechnic Institute, 208, 209, 211, 265

YMCA schools, 41, 44, 47, 54, 58–59, 64–65, 70–71, 266, 278, 279

Zapoleon, Marguerite, 119*n.*, 123